STANDARD GRADE

Craft & Design

course notes

Text © 2002 Peter Linton and Leo Norris
Design and layout © 2002 Leckie & Leckie Ltd
Cover image © Getty Images

06/111207

ISBN 978-1-84372-075-1

Published by
Leckie & Leckie Ltd, 3rd floor, 4 Queen Street, Edinburgh, EH2 1JE
Tel: 0131 220 6831 Fax: 0131 225 9987
enquiries@leckieandleckie.co.uk   www.leckieandleckie.co.uk

Edited by Mike Wood

Special thanks to Neil Arundel, Julie Barclay, Alison Irving, Caleb Rutherford (cover design), Lynsey Thompson and the Primary 1 pupils of Kinross Primary School.

A CIP Catalogue record for this book is available from the British Library.

Leckie & Leckie Ltd is a division of Huveaux plc.

CONTENTS

This book will help you to understand and enjoy the three elements of Standard Grade Craft and Design, which are:

- Designing
- Practical abilities
- Knowledge and Understanding.

These three elements have equal weighting in your final mark.

Together with your teacher's experience and advice, this book will support you throughout your course, helping you to:

- improve your understanding of the Design Process
- make the most of your creative skills
- organise and present your design project well
- plan and complete a major project
- work safely.

Section One:

Designing and Manufacturing your Project

The first section of this book (pages 4 to 32) gives useful advice about designing and manufacturing. Study this section before:

- selecting an interesting project to complete
- planning and completing each step in your design project
- beginning the manufacture of your project.

This section includes two completed design projects produced by pupils – one by Katy Galloway and the other by Ben Mathers. Katy's project is on pages 6 to 20 and Ben's project is on pages 21 to 32. The two projects follow the same Design Process, but use different styles, showing that there is no single way to solve a problem and present design work. Discuss both Ben's and Katy's projects with your teacher before deciding what style best suits you. They both represent Credit Level work and should be used to help you develop your own style. They should not be copied.

Katy is interested in design history, especially the Bauhaus. She has designed and made a CD organiser, basing her design on the style of the Bauhaus.

Section Two:

Knowledge and Understanding

Illustrated notes describing a wide range of tools, machine processes and materials are provided in the second section of this book (pages 33 to 48).

You will also find on the inside back cover checklists covering all the Knowledge and Understanding you need to know. Use these checklists to help you revise and prepare well for your exam.

There are also study tips on how to prepare for your exam on page 48.

Ben is a keen swimmer, who has designed and made a display unit for his medals. He developed a design based on the themes and patterns of swimming.

FINDING A GOOD PROJECT

Finding a good project is vital if you are to enjoy it and succeed in completing it well. A good project should:

- meet a real need
- offer scope for creativity
- be of interest to you
- be completed in the time allowed.

It is always better to complete a simple problem well than leave a complicated project unfinished. Bear in mind that a Credit Level project must have a reasonably demanding level of craftsmanship. Always get your teacher's advice on the final selection of your project.

Here are four ways to find a good project:

- Develop a theme
- Develop a personal interest
- Find a client
- Visit a local situation.

1. Develop a Theme

Consider all your needs.
Identify an area of personal interest, perhaps your hobby, and develop it in more detail. Ben has developed his hobby – swimming.

3. Find a Client

i.e. solve someone else's problem.

CLIENTS	PROJECTS
Local play group	Toys, games, play equipment
Museum	Display stand or case
Groups with special needs	Map for a blind person, holding device for an arthritic person

2. Develop a Personal Interest

Katy has chosen to develop her personal interest in Bauhaus. She identified the need to organise her CDs and trinkets and used her interest in design history to help develop a solution to this problem.

4. Visit a Local Situation

SITUATIONS
Sports centre

Shopping centre

Play area

Restaurant

While at a site, observe carefully, record what you see and try to identify problems you could solve to improve a small part of the situation.

THE DESIGN PROCESS

Your Craft and Design project requires you to understand and use the Design Process. The Design Process is a series of steps which take you from the Brief to Evaluation. There are many different ways of working through the Design Process. Ben has worked through the Design Process in a different way from Katy. However, both Ben and Katy have covered all the important steps to obtain a grade 1 at Credit Level.

Here is a diagram of the Design Process which Ben and Katy have used. More detailed explanations of each stage of this process can be found on the following pages:

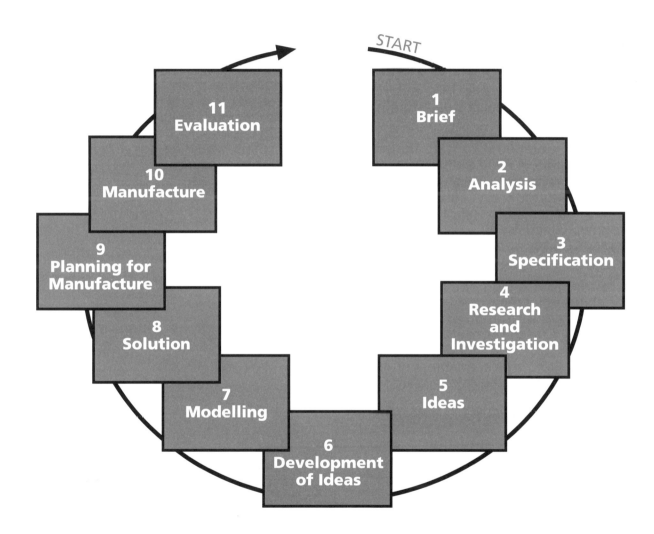

The **Design Brief** is the starting point of the **Design Process**. It is a short statement of what the problem is and gives the designer a 'lead-in' to the design project. The **Design Brief** is often written by a '**Client**' who has commissioned the design work.

You can write your own **Brief** but it is often better to find a client and ask the client to write one with you. However, you must be careful when the **Brief** is prepared.

Give enough information to state the problem clearly. If possible, outline a situation – perhaps an untidy room. Identify a need, e.g. 'to organise and store my untidy mess'. A Brief which says 'Design a container' is too open and does not give the designer a good 'lead-in'. 'Design a means of storing my CDs and trinkets' helps the designer by stating the main function of the design.

Don't restrict your design options by being too specific about what your design should do. For example, don't write 'Design a red box with a lid for storing my CDs and trinkets'. It restricts the design to a box with a lid without even considering a shelf, a rack, a cabinet or drawers. Choosing shapes, style and colours comes later in the Design Process.

TIPS
• If possible, identify a **client** and ask them to discuss a problem and write a brief with you.
• Write briefly about the situation which creates the problem and **identify the need.**
• State the problem **clearly.**
• Don't leave the Brief too open.
• State the **Primary Function** of the design.
• Don't be too specific – **keep your options open** at this stage.
• **Plan the layout** of the first page of your folio.
• **Leave room** for the Analysis and Specification.

Discussion with my clients

A chat with my mum and sister helped me identify a suitable project. We discussed several issues, including the mess in our bedroom. The bits and pieces that cause the mess include: **compact discs**, **pencils**, **coloured pencils**, **rubbers**, **sharpener** and **our diaries**. At night the problem gets worse when we have to find space for our **jewellery, watches** and **coins**. If I could design something to solve this problem our room would be tidy and Mum, my sister and I would be happy.

Finding a client

As my mum, my sister and I share the problem, I have asked them to be my '**clients**'. They have helped me prepare a Design Brief that I can work from. I will also check my design work with them at various stages in the design process.

CLIENTS' BRIEF

My sister and I share a bedroom that is getting more and more untidy by the day. Mum gets on at us constantly about the mess. The bits and pieces that cause the mess include: compact discs, pencils, coloured pencils, rubbers, sharpener and our diaries. At night the problem gets worse when we have to find space for our jewellery, watches and coins.
Design a storage device to help organise the mess and keep the room tidy.
The design should be functional, stylish and suitable for use in a teenager's room.

Mind mapping and brainstorming

Mind mapping can be used to think of questions that the designer will need in the **analysis**. A mind map starts with a central bubble which states the problem. Roads lead outwards from the centre. Each road is given the name of a **design factor**. (See page 33.)
Branches leading off the roads are made by adding words or statements that might influence the design factors. This is often done in a group and is known as **brainstorming**.

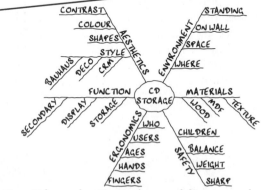

Don't be selective when adding words. Put down as many ideas as you can think of. Once the page is full of ideas you can select the important ones to use in your analysis.

Analysis

The Analysis is a way of breaking the problem down into all the things the designer must think about.

How do we analyse the problem?
First, break the problem into several parts. Then examine each part in turn. There are several ways of doing this. The method I have chosen uses **design factors**.

Design factors
I have chosen six **Design Factors** (see page 33) and prepared questions on these to ask my **clients**. I then recorded my clients' answers.

This will help me find out more about the design problem and give me a better idea of what my clients want.

Specification

The Analysis will help me write a Design Specification. A **Design Specification** is a list of what your design should do or be. It's sometimes called a Performance Specification. It's now that I begin making decisions about how my design should perform.

The specification will also become a checklist to measure your design work against as you progress through your folio. You must agree your **specification** with your **client**.

CLIENTS' BRIEF
My sister and I share a bedroom that is getting more and more untidy by the day. Mum gets on at us constantly about the mess. The bits and pieces that cause the mess include: compact discs, pencils, coloured pencils, rubbers, sharpener and our diaries. At night the problem gets worse when we have to find space for our jewellery, watches and coins.
Design a storage device to help organise the mess and keep the room tidy. The design should be functional, stylish and suitable for use in a teenager's room.

ANALYSIS I have prepared questions to ask my clients. My questions are all based on the 'Design Factors'. Ask your client at least one question for each design factor.

Function
Q. The primary function of the product is to organise and store the items listed in my client's brief. Will the product have a secondary function?
A. Yes, it should be decorative, nice to look at and colourful. We both feel that a product should function well and look good at the same time.

Aesthetics
Q. Should the product have a distinctive design style or colour scheme?
A. Yes, we both like simple geometric shapes and bold colours. We would like the design to incorporate these features.

Environment
Q. The product will be used in a bedroom. Should it be free-standing or wall mounted?
A. A free-standing design would work best because the wallspace is very limited. The design should be made to sit on a chest of drawers.

Ergonomics
Q. Who will use the product?
A. Our family, including two adults and our younger brother. Also my teenage friends. The design should be easy for adults and children to use.
Q. Should I make any special design considerations so that the product is easy to use?
A. Yes, the CDs must be easily identified and to remove from + replace in the device.

Materials + Construction
Q. Do you want the design to be made from a particular material or materials?
A. The materials and surface finish must be durable to withstand the wear and tear of use in a teenager's room. It should not be too expensive to build.

Safety
Q. Are there any special safety considerations?
A. Yes, it should be stable and not topple over. Also, pencils are dangerous when they are stored sticking up out of a pencil block. Our design should take account of these safety hazards.

SPECIFICATION
From the analysis I have decided that the design should:

- Have the primary function of storing and displaying CDs.
- Have a secondary function to be decorative; it must look good.
- Hold up to 40 compact discs, 6 pencils, a sharpener, rubber, 2 diaries and some trinkets and loose change.
- Store and display these items in a freestanding design.
- Be a suitable size and proportion to sit on the chest of drawers.
- Be a suitable size for children and adults to allow easy access to all items stored.
- Be safe to use, especially when storing sharp pencils, and be stable when full.
- Use materials that are cheap but enable me to make a durable and colourful project.
- Look very attractive. My clients like the Bauhaus style, especially their use of simple shapes and colours. I will investigate this style.

The **Research** and **Investigation** continues on from the **Analysis** and **Specification**. A look back at the last page shows that I have decided to store and display CDs, trinkets and pencils.

The research for this might include:
- measuring CDs
- working out how many I can store
- showing how I might rack or stack them
- working out how best to remove and replace them (how to access them).

The same can be done with the other items I am to store. I have filled my first research page with sketches and notes which mainly look at storage and display.

Most design work involves investigating **Ergonomics**. **Ergonomics** is the study of how we design things to suit our physical shape, size, movement and need for comfort. I have listed the Ergonomic considerations down one side of the page. I thought of:

- VISUAL CONSIDERATIONS
  I must be able to see my CDs and pencils.

- ACCESS CONSIDERATIONS
  I must be able to remove and replace my CDs and pencils easily.

I have recorded my research by sketching and writing notes. Try presenting your research this way. You may find you need more than one page.

Market Research

When a company is developing a new product **market research** helps them find out what consumers want. Market researchers ask members of the public questions about the product and often use a **prototype model** to show what the product looks and feels like.

The **market research** information is fed back to the **designer** who will then make the necessary **design modifications**. When a poduct is to be **mass produced** and the company is investing a great deal of money, the product must appeal to the consumer or it will not be successful.

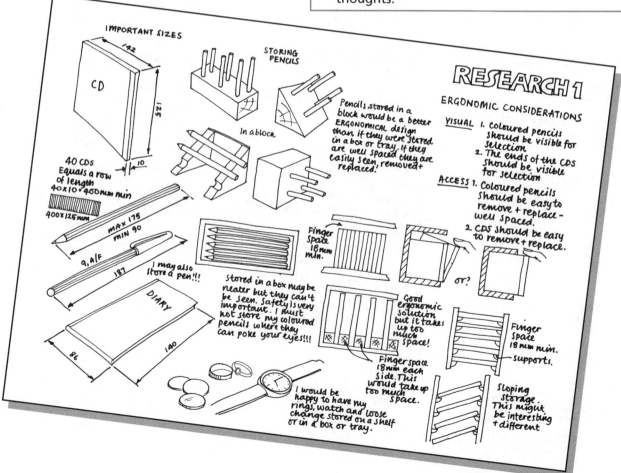

Sketching design ideas on paper is usually the most enjoyable part of producing your folio. Researching the history of design can be an exciting way of learning about design styles.

Various design movements occurred at different times in recent history. Each movement had its own style and personalities. There are lots to choose from, including:

Gothic   Arts and Crafts   Art Nouveau
Bauhaus   Art Deco   Fifties
Japanese   Pop Art
Charles Rennie Mackintosh

How do you find out about these movements and styles? What do they look like?
Your local library will have **reference books**, so will your school library and possibly your Craft & Design teacher.

The best plan is to have a look and decide which styles you like best.

I have picked a movement called the **Bauhaus**. The **Bauhaus** was a German university of design and creative arts. It existed from 1919 to 1933. They designed everything from buildings to furniture, posters to toys. Their ideas and influence are still important today.

The next step is to get a book and sift through it, sketching down designs and little bits of designs which you think reflect the Bauhaus. You are not actually designing anything yourself at this stage, only copying Bauhaus designs. This gives you a feel for their work and helps you practise your sketching skills.

Bauhaus designs were often based on three **simple shapes**: the **circle**, **square** and **triangle**. They gave each shape a colour: circle – blue, square – red, and triangle – yellow. I have looked for almost any design which uses these shapes and have called this sheet '**Bauhaus Visual References**'. I have added notes to say what I like about the designs and where they come from.

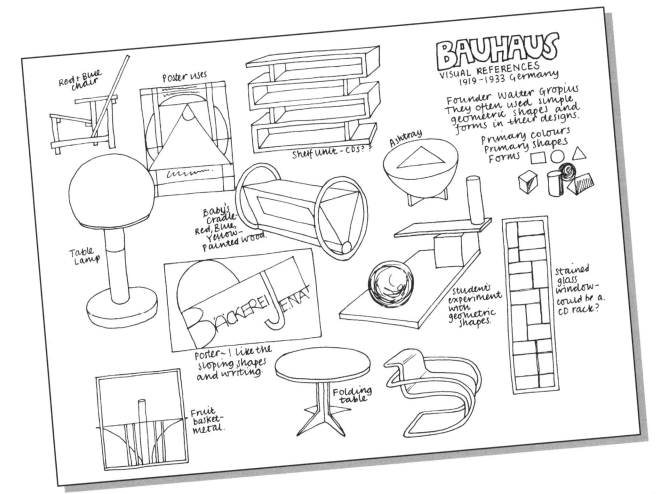

Many design styles are based on **shape**.

- **Charles Rennie Mackintosh** used **squares** and **ellipses**.
- **Art Nouveau** used elegant **curves** and **natural shapes**.
- The **Bauhaus** used **rectangles**, **circles** and **triangles**.

Designing can be made easier and more creative by using simple shapes as a starting point. Follow my tips, look at my example and try this in your project.

In my example I have played with the three geometric shapes, which the Bauhaus used, to create my own original ideas. I have also simplified some of the designs from my 'Visual References' page. You can do either or both. See if you can spot which ideas come from the previous page.

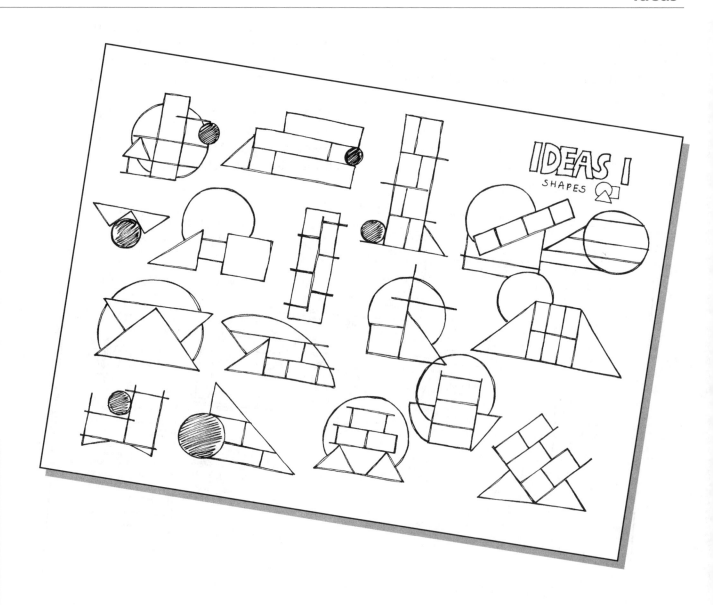

TIPS

- Build up ideas by **sketching quickly**. Don't pause, keep your pencil working and think while you sketch.
- **Sketch freehand** – a ruler slows you down.
- Keep your sketches **two-dimensional** only.
- **Don't rub out** bad ideas. Work on them. If they don't improve, ignore them.
- Join, overlap, add and subtract shapes.
- Use lines to join and **balance** your shapes.
- **Don't worry** about how you might build your designs. That comes later.

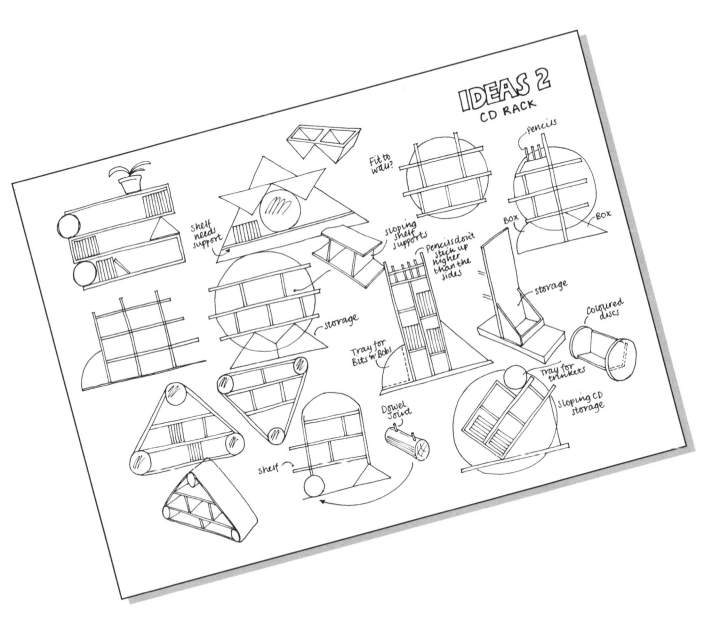

It is best not to fall into the trap of simply choosing to make one of your first ideas. These may seem promising but it is important to show that you can develop and improve on them.

My first ideas are a combination of simple shapes. On this sheet I have done four things:

1. **Selected** the ideas I like best.
2. Added thickness to lines to suggest **structure** and **material**.
3. Attempted to show how the designs **function**.
4. **Developed** and **improved** my first ideas.

At this stage I am hoping to reduce the number of ideas from about 16 to 3 or 4 good ones. However, even now I am being creative and new ideas still appear.

TIPS

- **Select** the best ideas from the previous sheet.
- Sketch them out giving lines a thickness to suggest **structure**. Keep most of the sketches 2-D.
- Improve your ideas by making **small changes**. Combine them with other ideas, add new bits and leave out bits that don't work.
- Remember your designs should be **functional**. If possible, **show your designs in use**.
- Experiment with **colour**, **proportion** and **shape**. Small changes here can make all the difference.

By now you should be focusing on **one idea**. We need to concentrate on that and **work towards a solution**. Your sketches should be **more detailed**, perhaps showing possible **joints** or how the various parts may **function**. Remember that you are still being creative, still trying to improve your design.

In my example, I have selected one basic design: shelves in front of a circular back. I have tried to work out the best arrangement of these two elements.

I have used three sheets for my creative work (ideas). You might need two, three, four or even more: it depends on you and your project. Three sheets give enough scope for creative work and design development without going 'over the top'.

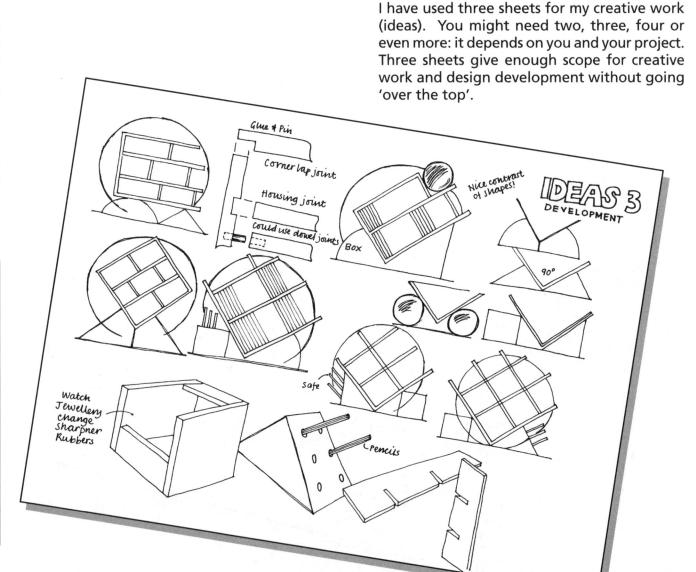

TIPS

- Keep sketching. Drawing with instruments slows down your creativity.
- Use **sketches and notes** to explain how you might join parts together and which **materials** you might use. Take advice from your teacher on this.
- Show how your design functions and looks. Experiment with colour – it can make a big difference.
- Continue making changes, e.g. adding bits and **changing proportions**.
- Consider making a simple **card model**. It can really help sort out the problems. (See next page.)
- Keep checking your designs against the specification.

A design model is a 3-D mock-up of a possible design solution. Designers build models to **test**, **develop** and **communicate** design ideas.

Design modelling is an important part of your Craft & Design course. A quick card model can help you sort out many design problems.

There are four main types of design model:
- **concept models** – built during design development to test an idea
- **block models** – built during design development to show a client
- **prototype models** – built to scale after the working drawing
- **3-D computer models** – drawn during design development to show a client and to generate the working drawings.

Concept Model

You can make a concept model quickly using **inexpensive materials** such as cardboard, polystyrene board or balsa wood. A concept model usually **tests** the **construction** of your design and helps work out how your design **might be manufactured**. It may only test a small part of your design such as a joint.

Block Model

Block models are so-called because they are often cut from a **solid block** of polystyrene, balsa wood or clay. They are often painted and may have details such as switches or buttons added. New telephones or calculators may be modelled in this way to **test** the **ergonomics** and **aesthetics** of a design.

Prototype Model

Eventually a **working model** may have to be made. Such a model is called a **prototype**. It is usually actual size and is made of the same materials as the full production product. The prototype **tests all aspects of the design** from **ergonomics** and **aesthetics** to **manufacture**, **assembly** and **function**.

3-D Computer Model

Today designers often produce 3-D computer drawings of their designs. **3-D computer models** can be rotated to be viewed from any angle and can be **rendered** (coloured and shaded) to look realistic. They are **quick** and **cheap** to produce, and can be modified easily.

I have just completed the ideas pages in my folio. I still have to produce a **working drawing** with all the **sizes**, etc. Before I do all that work I want to test my design. The most appropriate model for my purposes is the quick, inexpensive concept model. Made from cardboard, it slots and glues together.

TIPS
• Design models can be made at almost any stage in the Design Process.
• You may find you will make more than one.
• Take care with cutting tools and glues.
• Ask your teacher's advice about suitable modelling materials and techniques.
• A quick cheap model can be worth a thousand sketches.

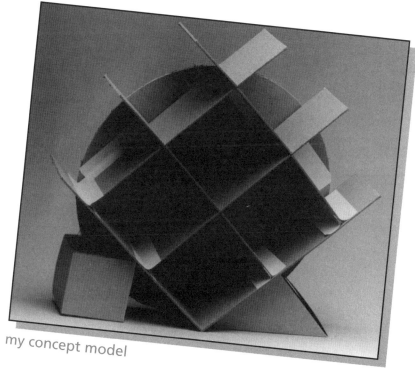

my concept model

The solution should show three things:

1. A **clear sketch** or **drawing** of your chosen design.

2. **Sketches** and **notes** to show how it **works** and **fits together**.

3. Notes to **justify** why you think this is your best design.

A **working drawing** is required to help you **manufacture** your design. It should show **dimensions** and **details** of all the parts and **joints**. It usually consists of orthographic drawings such as front elevation, end elevation and plan. These drawings are normally **drawn to scale** and this can be difficult.

A **full-size drawing** will give you a much better idea of how your design will look. Discuss this drawing with your teacher. You will need his or her advice.

It is easier to make changes at this stage. You can use this full-size drawing to help you make a **scaled-down** working drawing. Your teacher may recommend that you also make a scaled-down drawing with more views.

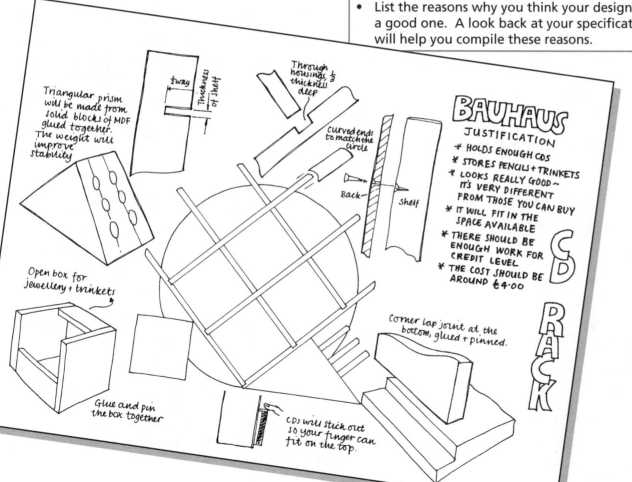

Triangular prism will be made from solid blocks of MDF glued together. The weight will improve stability

Open box for jewellery + trinkets

Glue and pin the box together

Through housings ⅓ thickness deep

Curved ends to match the circle

Back — Shelf

CDs will stick out so your finger can fit on the top.

Corner lap joint at the bottom, glued + pinned.

BAUHAUS
JUSTIFICATION
* HOLDS ENOUGH CDS
* STORES PENCILS + TRINKETS
* LOOKS REALLY GOOD ~ IT'S VERY DIFFERENT FROM THOSE YOU CAN BUY
* IT WILL FIT IN THE SPACE AVAILABLE
* THERE SHOULD BE ENOUGH WORK FOR CREDIT LEVEL
* THE COST SHOULD BE AROUND £4.00

CD RACK

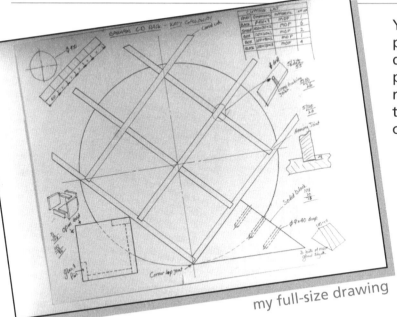

my full-size drawing

Your teacher will give you a price for each part. It is often the case that several different materials are suitable for your project. Some materials are expensive so make sure you cost your project before the material is cut. Write down the costings in your folio.

The **Cutting List** is a table showing which materials are to be used, and what sizes the various parts are cut to, before the product can be shaped and put together.

Cutting Lists are used in building and engineering industries every day. They are also used to **cost** a project. Measuring your **full-size drawing** will help you compile your cutting list.

Part	Dimensions length, breadth, thickness	Material	No. of	Cost
BACK	430 × 430 × 12	MDF	1	60p
SHELF 1	385 × 130 × 12	MDF	1	30p
SHELF 2	420 × 130 × 12	MDF	1	30p
SHELF 3	388 × 130 × 12	MDF	1	30p

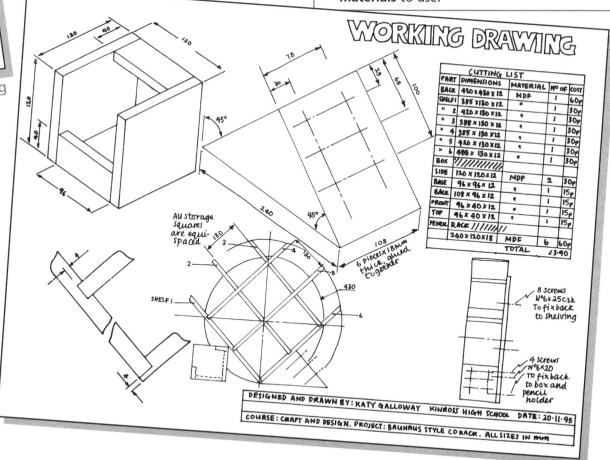

Your **sequence of operations** is the third and final part of the **planning** for **manufacture**. The sequence of operations is really just a list of what you need to do to construct your design. Sketches can be added to help explain your procedure.

At Credit Level this list needs to be quite detailed. The size of your list depends on how complex your design is. As a rough guide, you might aim for 12 to 16 steps.

Writing a sequence of operations from start to finish can be difficult. Discuss this with your teacher. He or she may suggest that you plan out four main stages in advance. Then plan the more detailed steps as you go along.

The main stages in any sequence of operations should include:
- **marking out**
- **cutting**, **drilling** and **shaping**
- **assembling**
- **finishing**.

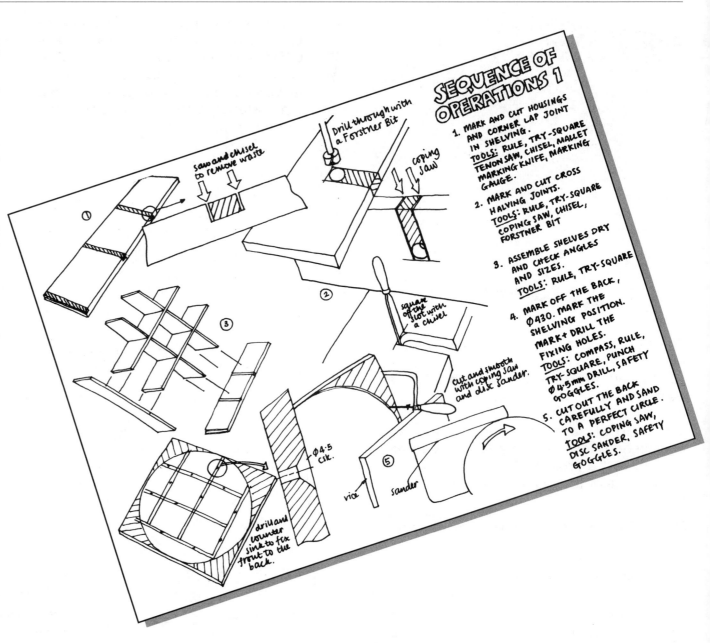

My sequence of operations includes steps which you would expect in most folios, e.g. 'assemble shelves dry and check angles and sizes'.

The **order** of your list is very important. There are some things which must be done before others. Take your teacher's advice on this.

Sketches are really helpful. They can make the steps easier to understand. Keep your sketches simple and add notes as required.

Making brief notes of the tools and equipment you will need helps you organise your time in the workshop.

You should have your **working drawing** and **sequence of operations** on your bench when you are making your project.

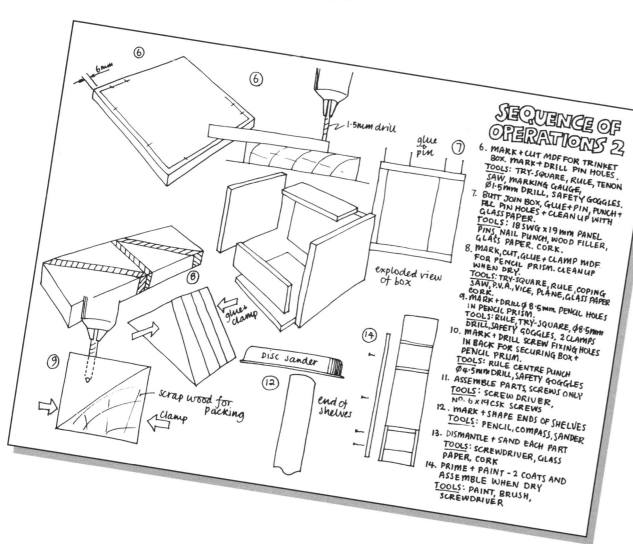

SEQUENCE OF OPERATIONS 2

6. MARK + CUT MDF FOR TRINKET BOX. MARK + DRILL PIN HOLES.
   TOOLS: TRY-SQUARE, RULE, TENON SAW, MARKING GAUGE, Ø1·5mm DRILL, SAFETY GOGGLES.

7. BUTT JOIN BOX, GLUE + PIN, PUNCH + FILL PIN HOLES + CLEAN UP WITH GLASS PAPER.
   TOOLS: 18 SWG × 19mm PANEL PINS, NAIL PUNCH, WOOD FILLER, GLASS PAPER, CORK.

8. MARK, CUT, GLUE + CLAMP MDF FOR PENCIL PRISM. CLEAN UP WHEN DRY.
   TOOLS: TRY-SQUARE, RULE, COPING SAW, P.V.A., VICE, PLANE, GLASS PAPER CORK.

9. MARK + DRILL Ø 8·5mm PENCIL HOLES IN PENCIL PRISM.
   TOOLS: RULE, TRY-SQUARE, Ø8·5mm DRILL, SAFETY GOGGLES, 2 CLAMPS

10. MARK + DRILL SCREW FIXING HOLES IN BACK FOR SECURING BOX + PENCIL PRISM.
    TOOLS: RULE CENTRE PUNCH Ø4·5mm DRILL, SAFETY GOGGLES

11. ASSEMBLE PARTS, SCREWS ONLY
    TOOLS: SCREW DRIVER, NO. 6 × 19 CSK SCREWS

12. MARK + SHAPE ENDS OF SHELVES
    TOOLS: PENCIL, COMPASS, SANDER

13. DISMANTLE + SAND EACH PART
    TOOLS: SCREWDRIVER, GLASS PAPER, CORK

14. PRIME + PAINT – 2 COATS AND ASSEMBLE WHEN DRY
    TOOLS: PAINT, BRUSH, SCREWDRIVER

6mm

1·5mm drill

glue & pin

exploded view of box

glue & clamp

DISC SANDER

end of shelves

scrap wood for packing

Clamp

TIPS

- Set out the **four main stages** and plan three or four steps under each stage.
- Ask your teacher how much you need to do to get started.
- Set out your page so that it is easy to follow.
- **Number** each step to make the order clear.
- Sketch out the important steps. Keep the sketches simple. Don't overdo sketches of tools and equipment.
- List the **main tools** and **equipment** you will need at each step.
- Check each step with your teacher. His or her opinion will save you valuable time and effort.

Often the designer has to use his or her skills to sell ideas to a **client** or **customer**. One of the simplest ways of doing this is by making a **presentation drawing**.

This drawing or sketch should give the untrained customer a good idea of what the design will look like when it is made. The most realistic type of drawing is perspective but you can use an isometric or even a 2-D drawing.

The CD rack would be very difficult to draw in either perspective or isometric. I have saved time and effort by tracing a 2-D drawing I made earlier in the folio.

The presentation drawing can double as a front cover for the folio. I produced mine after I did my working drawing.

TIPS

- Make a good, **clear drawing** or **sketch**.
- Show your design **in use** if you can.
- Add **colour** to make it clear and realistic.
- A snappy title in a contrasting colour can be tucked in behind the drawing to **add depth**.
- Keep the background very simple, like our coloured **flashbar** – again in a **contrasting colour**.
- Plan your work to fill the page and add your name.
- Avoid bold, diagonal text or flashbars. They dominate the page and confuse the viewer.

The manufacturing of your project is one third of your course assessment. Like the other two parts, **Designing**, and **Knowledge and Understanding**, manufacturing must be carefully thought through, planned and studied.

You will have spent much of the previous year learning craft skills and gaining knowledge about materials, tools and processes.

For most pupils, making their project is the most enjoyable part of the course. Follow our tips and have fun while you learn.

TIPS

- **Plan** your manufacture carefully by producing a Working Drawing, Cutting List and a Sequence of Operations.
- Mark out **accurately**.
- Cut, shape and drill **carefully**.
- If it is to be assembled permanently (e.g. by gluing, welding or brazing), **assemble it dry** first and ask your teacher to check it.
- Spend time applying a **high quality finish**. Don't skimp on sanding and cleaning. Apply varnish and paint carefully.
- Ask your **teacher's advice** at each stage of manufacture.
- Always **work safely**. Learn the safety rules especially for using machinery and tools.

manufacturing my CD organiser

my finished product

Evaluating in Craft & Design means 'checking the quality of what you have designed'. Perhaps without knowing it you have been evaluating your work right through the Design Process.

You have evaluated:
- your Analysis
- your choice of ideas
- even the layout of each page in your folio.

The final Evaluation comes after the design has been constructed. There are several ways of doing this. I have looked back to my **Design Specification** (page 7) and evaluated my model against each item on the specification.

TIPS

- Consider each item in the **Design Specification** and ask: **'Does my design do that?'**
- Write down your answers. State how well or badly your model satisfies each item.
- Include clear sketches to highlight the good and bad points of your design.
- Ask one additional question: 'If I were to make my model again, would I make improvements?'
- Don't be afraid to criticise your own design. You will not be marked down for this – indeed it may show that you have been thorough.
- Finally, it can be helpful to give each item in your evaluation a **star rating**, usually a score out of five. This states clearly whether you think it succeeds or fails.

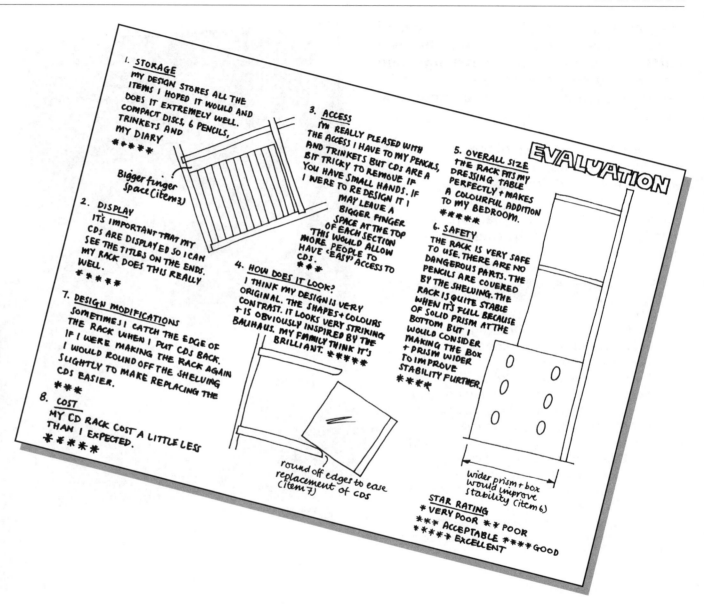

1. STORAGE
MY DESIGN STORES ALL THE ITEMS I HOPED IT WOULD AND DOES IT EXTREMELY WELL. COMPACT DISCS, 6 PENCILS, TRINKETS AND MY DIARY
✱✱✱✱✱

Bigger finger space (item 3)

2. DISPLAY
IT'S IMPORTANT THAT MY CDS ARE DISPLAYED SO I CAN SEE THE TITLES ON THE ENDS. MY RACK DOES THIS REALLY WELL.
✱✱✱✱✱

3. ACCESS
I'M REALLY PLEASED WITH THE ACCESS I HAVE TO MY PENCILS, AND TRINKETS BUT CDS ARE A BIT TRICKY TO REMOVE IF YOU HAVE SMALL HANDS. IF I WERE TO REDESIGN IT I MAY LEAVE A BIGGER FINGER SPACE AT THE TOP OF EACH SECTION THIS WOULD ALLOW MORE PEOPLE TO HAVE 'EASY' ACCESS TO CDS.
✱✱✱

4. HOW DOES IT LOOK?
I THINK MY DESIGN IS VERY ORIGINAL. THE SHAPES + COLOURS CONTRAST. IT LOOKS VERY STRIKING + IS OBVIOUSLY INSPIRED BY THE BAUHAUS. MY FAMILY THINK IT'S BRILLIANT. ✱✱✱✱✱

5. OVERALL SIZE
THE RACK FITS MY DRESSING TABLE PERFECTLY + MAKES A COLOURFUL ADDITION TO MY BEDROOM.
✱✱✱✱✱

6. SAFETY
THE RACK IS VERY SAFE TO USE. THERE ARE NO DANGEROUS PARTS. THE PENCILS ARE COVERED BY THE SHELVING. THE RACK IS QUITE STABLE WHEN ITS FULL BECAUSE OF SOLID PRISM AT THE BOTTOM BUT I WOULD CONSIDER MAKING THE BOX + PRISM WIDER TO IMPROVE STABILITY FURTHER.
✱✱✱✱

7. DESIGN MODIFICATIONS
SOMETIMES I CATCH THE EDGE OF THE RACK WHEN I PUT CDS BACK. IF I WERE MAKING THE RACK AGAIN I WOULD ROUND OFF THE SHELVING SLIGHTLY TO MAKE REPLACING THE CDS EASIER.
✱✱✱

8. COST
MY CD RACK COST A LITTLE LESS THAN I EXPECTED.
✱✱✱✱✱

round off edges to ease replacement of CDs (item 7)

wider prism + box would improve stability (item 6)

STAR RATING
✱ VERY POOR ✱✱ POOR
✱✱✱ ACCEPTABLE ✱✱✱✱ GOOD
✱✱✱✱✱ EXCELLENT

Introduction

A good introduction to a design project should explain what the problem is that needs solving, i.e. why is your project needed?

The introduction can be presented in a number of ways, e.g.

- A written statement
- A letter from a 'client', who has a problem that needs to be solved
- A photograph showing a situation
- Drawings to illustrate a problem
- A survey that shows a need to improve something.

In other words, any good way of describing a situation clearly.

Brief

As the word suggests, the **Brief** should be a **short, clear statement of what you intend to do**.

Analysis

The **Analysis** is simply a way of **breaking the problem down** into all the things the designer must think about. The headings Ben has used come from the Design Factors checklist on page 33.

Specification

The **Specification** is a **list of qualities that your project should have** if it is to work well and be a success, i.e. it specifies what you want to achieve.

TIPS

The headings in the analysis will vary from one problem to another, but the simple questions:

- Who?
- What?
- Why?
- Where?
- How?

will often get you off to a good start. Try to fill out each heading by listing things that will affect the design or things you will need to find out. The analysis can be presented as a **Mind Map** or as **a series of Headings and Lists as it is here**.

TIPS

- **For every heading** in your analysis, **specify a target** to match it.
- **Avoid vague targets** like 'it must look good', or 'it must be well made'.
- Specify **why** it must look good or be well made, e.g. 'it should look attractive so people will notice it'.
- Use the **Design Factors** on page 33 to start your Analysis.

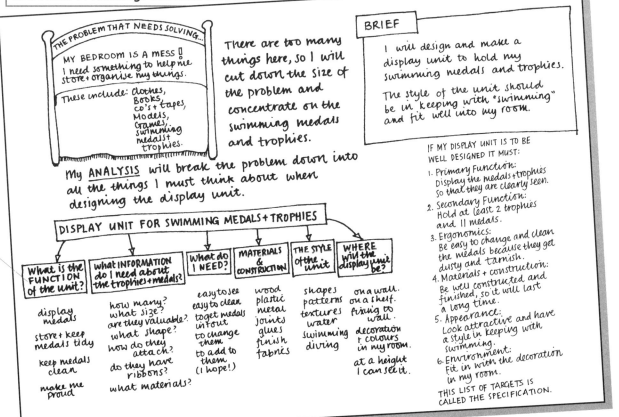

To help you **organise** and **structure** your design work you will need to plan:

a) **What** you need to do

b) The **order** in which you will do things.

Here is one method you may find useful. To get started, use your **Specification** to create a **Design Plan**.

Firstly, decide what you need to **investigate** to achieve each target on your Specification. This may involve:

- collecting useful information (researching)
- sketching and noting ideas
- looking at alternative ways of doing things
- exploring things like colours, patterns and textures
- making decisions
- giving reasons.

Your design work will be a record of these investigations.

Secondly, decide on the **order** in which you will investigate each section. In this case I will start with collecting information about the medals and trophies and presenting it in the form of drawings, sizes and notes. **Get advice from your teacher** about the best order for you. Getting this right should make the designing easier and avoid frustrations.

Thirdly, think about how you are going to **present your design work** and record this in very simple sketches and notes.

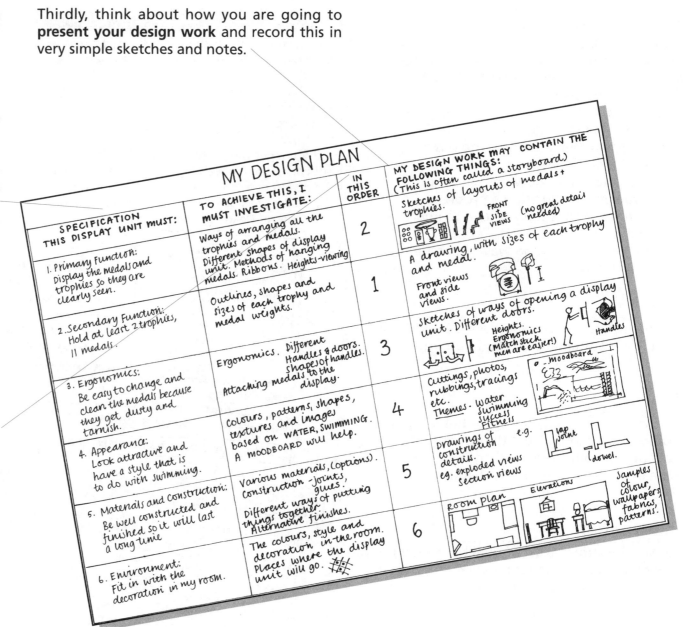

A good investigation should contain a record of any **research, information, ideas** and **tests** you need **to help you make decisions** about the design of your final solution.

Each section should be clearly headed and set out on the page, with possibly two or three sections to a page.

SECTION 1: THE MEDALS AND TROPHIES
I have drawn simple side views and recorded the sizes, materials and useful details about the medals and trophies.

SECTION 2: DISPLAYING THE MEDALS
Even at this stage, ideas will begin to emerge. In this case I have concentrated only on different ways of arranging the medals and types of surfaces to put them on.

SECTION 3: ERGONOMICS
I have recorded ergonomic considerations to do with seeing, handling and using the display unit. Different types of project will have other ergonomic considerations, so think about what is best for yours.

TIPS

- Use **quick annotated sketches,** with lots of useful information and notes to show what you are thinking about.
- Use **coloured pencils** to apply only as much colour as you need to help explain things clearly.
- Use **different views**, e.g. front, side, plan and section views.
- **Don't score things out** or rework a sheet to 'best' quality.
- **Fill up the page!**
- Try to **show different ways of doing things**. This will make it easier for you to make good decisions later on.

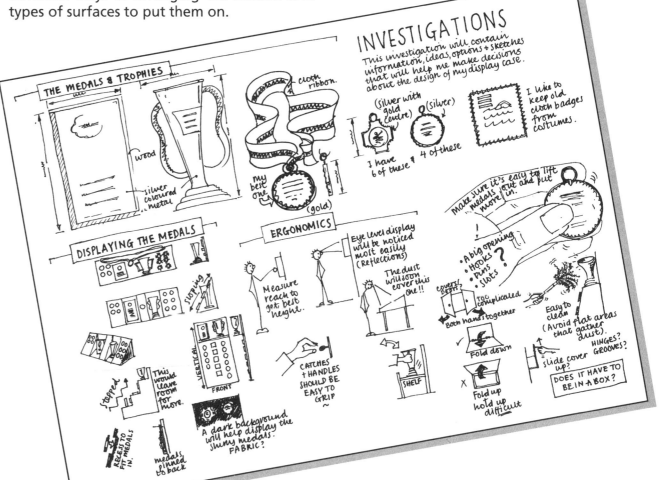

Moodboarding is a technique used by designers to investigate appearance and help them **think of and use creative ideas**. A moodboard is a **collection of visual material connected to a theme**. The themes in this case are water, fitness and swimmers. A moodboard may contain:

- cuttings from magazines
- photographs
- photocopies
- sketches
- samples of materials with interesting colours and textures.

You may need to:
- use your library
- collect specialist magazines
- photograph things.

Make notes on your moodboard to record colours, patterns, shapes and textures that you find interesting. These often provide **inspiration for creative ideas** that you would normally never have thought of and help to give your project a truly **creative input**.

A moodboard is **not** a collection of pictures of products you would like to make, e.g. pictures of cassette racks and display units.

my moodboard

TIP
• When selecting material, choose a theme that is connected to your project, e.g.

Project	Theme
Storage for music cassettes	Music you like, bands, dancing
Educational toy for children	Play, fun, numbers, symbols
Display for cosmetics	Colours, smells, fashion

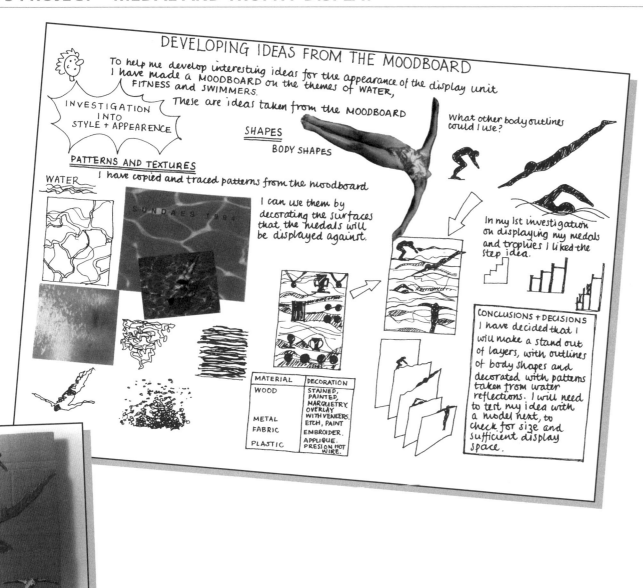

One of the targets I set myself in my specification was to design an attractive display unit with a style in keeping with swimming.

My moodboard has provided me with a way to investigate style and appearance. I have looked for interesting **colours**, **patterns**, **textures** and **shapes**. The bits I like have been **traced**, **drawn or photocopied**.

For example, the outline of the diving body has helped me think of three other swimming body shapes. These have been combined with patterns and colours based on reflections in water.

my simple card model

TIPS

- It is only now that a possible solution begins to emerge.
- **Test** that idea straight away with a simple model using, for example, corrugated box card. This will help you to make a decision, although the idea will still need a lot of developing.
- **Modelling** is a vital part of designing. It makes it much easier for you to:
  - test out an idea
  - see what an idea looks like
  - work out important sizes
  - decide how it will be constructed.

Now I have a good idea for a solution, I need to **develop it into a working solution** by investigating possible **materials** and **constructions**.

To do this, I need to work out more detailed sizes. I have done this by making an **accurate model**. A range of **construction methods** and **materials** has been considered. (Again, I might test them with a model of, say, a joint.)

TIPS

- **Sectioned and exploded views** are useful ways of showing how things work or are put together.
- This is a good opportunity to show how much you know about **materials, construction methods** and **finishes**.
- You need to be more **detailed and careful** with your **drawings** now.
- **Colour coding** the parts can make the drawings clearer.

my models to develop ideas

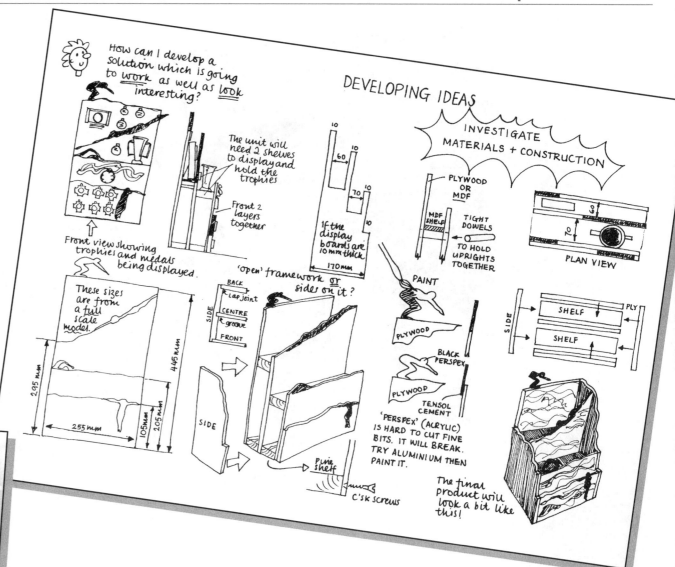

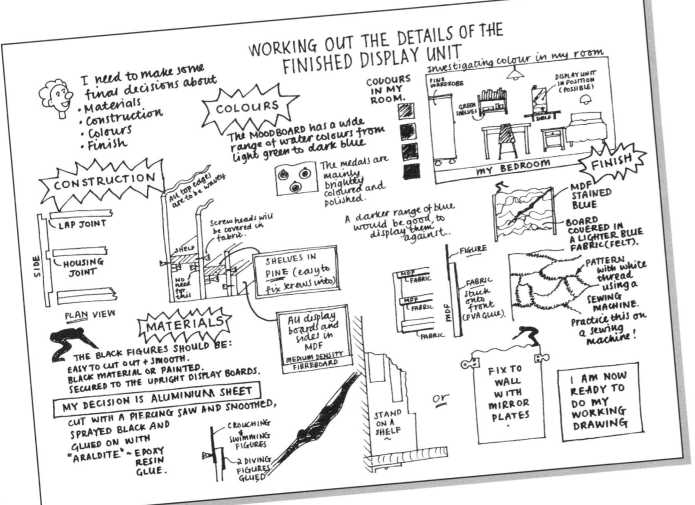

This is the part of your project which needs the **final decisions** to be made about the details of your solution. These decisions will be concerned with:

- shapes
- colours
- sizes
- construction details
- materials
- finishes.

Only when all these decisions are made can you go on to complete a **working drawing**.

Even at this stage in this project, investigations are being made into the colour scheme and finish, so the display unit fits in well with the decoration in the room where it will be used.

TIPS

- When making a decision, try to **record why** you have made it. This is a good way of showing your understanding of materials, their working properties and good design.
- Keep checking your decisions against your **specification**.
- **Seek the advice of your teacher**. His or her experience can often save you using up valuable time on things that simply won't work.
- **Modelling**, again, has an important role to play here. For example, a card model finished in the proposed colour scheme and pinned to the wall where the display unit is to be kept will help you decide if the colours are right or not.

A good **working drawing** should have enough useful information in it to enable someone else to make the product completely and successfully.

The important information in a working drawing should include:
- what the product looks like
- materials
- sizes
- construction details
- finish.

There are no set rules for presenting a working drawing as long as the information is clear and easy to understand.

TIPS

- This working drawing uses an **exploded pictorial view** which has been carefully sketched. (It did not require drawing instruments.) Details have been added with other small drawings and notes.
- A **cutting list** has been added to show how much material is needed for the product.
- Remember that this list has your **total material requirements**, e.g. the total amount of MDF for the four display boards has been calculated. This avoids listing every item in your product made from the same material.

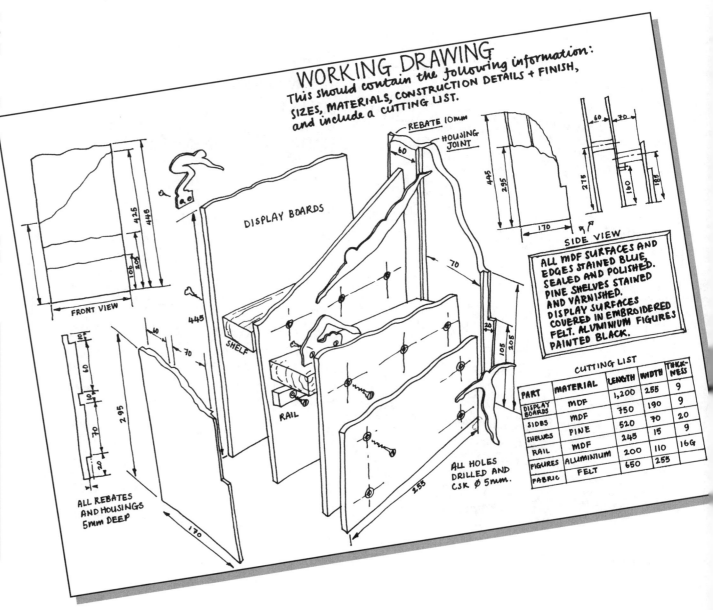

WORKING DRAWING
This should contain the following information:
SIZES, MATERIALS, CONSTRUCTION DETAILS + FINISH, and include a CUTTING LIST.

ALL MDF SURFACES AND EDGES STAINED BLUE, SEALED AND POLISHED. PINE SHELVES STAINED AND VARNISHED. DISPLAY SURFACES COVERED IN EMBROIDERED FELT. ALUMINIUM FIGURES PAINTED BLACK.

ALL HOLES DRILLED AND CSK Ø 5mm.

ALL REBATES AND HOUSINGS 5mm DEEP

CUTTING LIST				
PART	MATERIAL	LENGTH	WIDTH	THICKNESS
DISPLAY BOARDS	MDF	1,200	255	9
SIDES	MDF	750	190	9
SHELVES	PINE	520	70	20
RAIL	MDF	245	15	9
FIGURES	ALUMINIUM	200	110	16G
FABRIC	FELT	650	255	

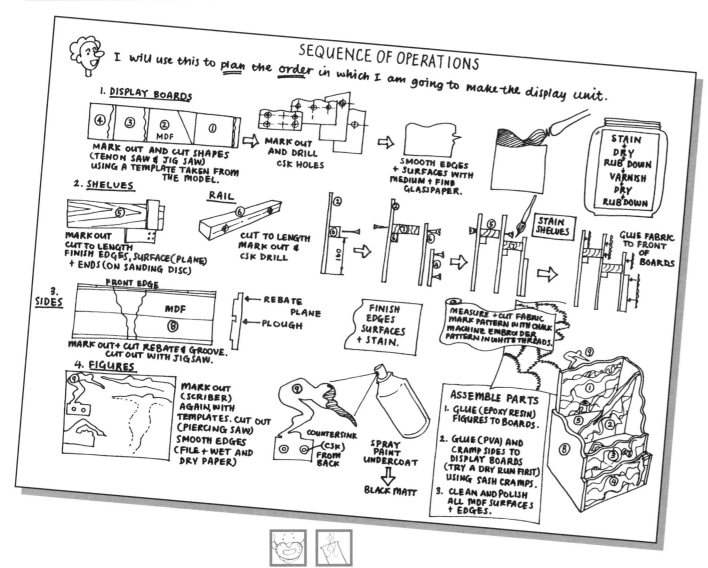

When using any aerosol spray paint, always observe safety procedures – wear a face mask and work in a well ventilated area.

The **sequence of operations** is a useful way to plan how you are going to make your product.

By planning ahead, you can decide:

- the **order** in which you will tackle the making tasks

- what **materials** you will need to complete each stage

- what **tools**, **equipment** and **machinery** will be needed.

Good planning will avoid delays, help you to organise and use your time well, and enable you to complete your model in the 20 to 25 hours available to you.

One third of your course assessment is based on the quality of the finished product.

It is important that you manufacture your product to the very best of your ability, using a range of the skills and techniques learnt during your course.

Use these tips to help you make the most of your skills.

TIPS

- Always **plan ahead**. Your sequence of operatons will help you do this.
- **Measure and mark** out with great care.
- Select the **best tools** and **machines** for each job and follow correct procedures.
- Check with your teacher if you are in doubt.
- Aim to achieve the best quality of **fit** and **finish** on your model.
- Work **safely**.
- Even at this stage you might **change** part of your design to make it work better. This is all right but remember to **record** any change and include this information in your **evaluation**.

manufacturing my medal and trophy display

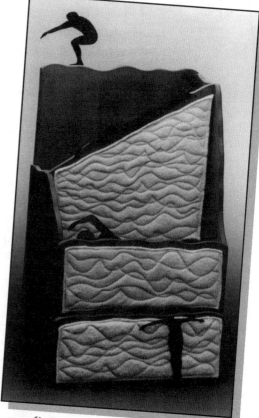

my finished product

When any product has been designed and made to solve a problem, the question '**Has the problem been solved**?' must be answered before the Design Process is complete. Designers and their clients carry out an **evaluation** to check:

- If all the targets set out in the original specification have been met.

- If there are any improvements that can be made to make the solution work better.

These improvements may arise because the product does not work properly or look right or there may have been problems during manufacture.

A good evaluation will highlight **strengths** as well as **weaknesses** in a design.

Very often designers are asked to improve an existing product, so an evaluation may in fact be used to start a Design Process as well as complete it.

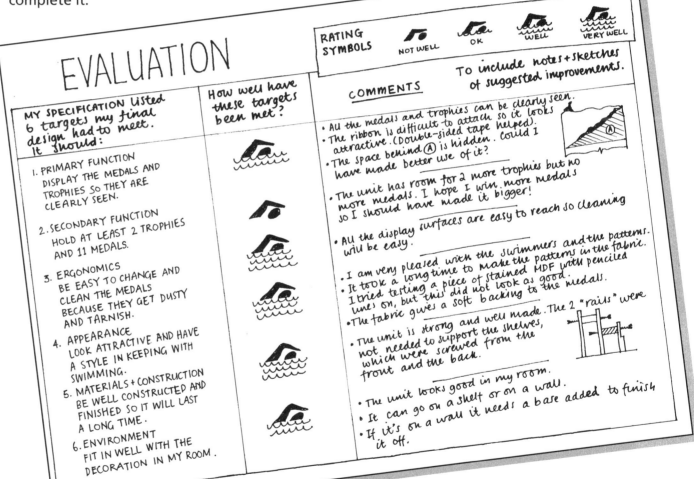

TIPS

- **Start** your **evaluation** by listing all the targets you set in your **specification** and do the evaluation one target at a time.
- **Rating symbols** can help you to say how each target has been met. (Designing these symbols can be an interesting graphic design task.)
- Think carefully about how you can **test** your product to see how well a target has been met. Would other people's opinions help? Try the product where it will be used.
- Explain **how** you arrived at your decisions.
- Use clear, annotated sketches to help make your comments and **show improvements**.

The front cover for your project is normally done last. Once completed, each page can be checked, put in the correct order, then made into a booklet by stapling or using a slide or comb binder.

CRAFT & DESIGN PROJECT •
SWIMMING TROPHY
DISPLAY UNIT

BEN MATHERS • 4C2

The cover should have a clear **title** on it stating what your project is.

Include your name and class. Printing can be produced by hand, with stencils, or on a computer.

There is no requirement for you to use an illustration on the cover, but it is a good opportunity to improve the **presentation** of your project.

Decide what type of illustration you would like to use. For this project I could have chosen any of the following:

- A presentation drawing of the product, either pictorial or orthographic.

- A photograph of the finished product.

- A drawing or photograph of a trophy or medal.

- A decorative panel based on body shapes and water patterns.

An **index** on the inside of the cover will help to show a good structure and make it easy to find different sections of the project folio.

KNOWLEDGE AND UNDERSTANDING OF DESIGN

Design Factors Checklist

Design Factors

In your Knowledge and Understanding exam you will be asked to look at real products and explain which Design Factors were considered when the products were created. Our Design Factors Checklist will help you answer these questions. Try it now. Which Design Factors from our Checklist would the designer of this mountain bike have considered before finalising his or her design?

Design Factors Checklist

These Design Factors will need to be considered whenever you **analyse** a problem. (This checklist could also be used when **evaluating** whether a product is well-designed or not.)

ESSENTIAL INFORMATION

- When designers solve problems, there are important things they must think about. To make it easier to solve, they **break the problem down into smaller parts (Design Factors)** and consider each one in turn. This is called the **Analysis**. It helps the designer to learn enough about the problem to write a **Design Specification**.
- The Design Specification is a list of things which the final design should do or be.
- The Design Factors we have chosen apply to any design project. Try to remember the **seven** factors in our checklist.

1. FUNCTION
What should the product **do**? It may have one important, **primary function** and several **secondary functions**, such as fashion or style.

2. ERGONOMICS
Who will use the product? Will it be used by **arms, legs, hands, eyes**, etc? Will it be used sitting, standing, or for working with? Can it be designed to adjust for **comfort** or **safety**?

3. AESTHETICS
Is it important that the product **looks good**? Consider: **colour, shape, form, proportion, line, texture, balance, fashion** and **style**.

4. ENVIRONMENT
Will it be used **indoors** or **outdoors**? Should it **blend in** with or **stand out** from its environment? Could it be designed to be more **environmentally friendly**? Will it need to withstand **extreme conditions**?

5. MATERIALS AND CONSTRUCTION
What are the most suitable **materials for the job**? Should they be **strong, durable, soft, warm**? Must they be **rigid** or **collapsible** or have **moving parts**? Can the product be **mass-produced**?

6. SAFETY
What safety features have been built into the design? How can it be made **safer to use**? Does it conform to **British Safety Standards**?

7. COST
Will the product be **expensive** or **inexpensive to make**? **Who** will want to buy it? Is it cheaper or more expensive than its **competitors**? How much will it **cost to run**?

Ergonomics

Ergonomics is the **study of people in relation to their surroundings and the products they use.** The designer uses ergonomics to design products and spaces that **match** the needs of the people who will use them.

Any product, system or environment that has been ergonomically designed will be **comfortable, safe** and **easy to use**.

Designers often use a scaled-down, plastic figure called an **'ergonome'** to achieve this.

Here are some examples of ergonomics in action:

Headphones must fit comfortably over the user's head and ears. The controls should be easy to reach and adjust.

This Dyson upright carpet cleaner can tilt to be pushed easily.

Examples of how Anthropometrics are used:
A door should allow 95th %le (male) to get through.
A kettle, when full, to be carried by 5th %le (female).

Anthropometrics

Anthropometrics is concerned with the **measurements** of the **shapes** and **sizes of people** and the **range of their movements**.
Products will work better if they match the sizes of the people who will use them.

Designers need to know **who** they are designing for so they can **research** and collect useful information. They may have to make their own measurements or study an **anthropometric table** like this:

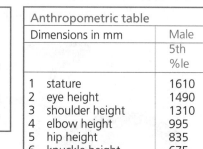

| Anthropometric table | | | | | | |
| Dimensions in mm | Male | | | Female | | |
	5th %le	50th %le	95th %le	5th %le	50th %le	95th %le
1 stature	1610	1735	1855	1520	1620	1715
2 eye height	1490	1615	1740	1410	1510	1610
3 shoulder height	1310	1420	1530	1225	1315	1405
4 elbow height	995	1080	1170	930	1005	1080
5 hip height	835	915	995	750	820	885
6 knuckle height	675	745	815	665	720	780
7 fingertip height	555	625	695	550	610	665

Anthropometric estimates for
15- to 18-year-old British children.

5TH – 95TH PERCENTILE

Products are normally designed to fit a **range of sizes** of people, e.g. a seat on a bus must hold a variety of sizes and weights of traveller. The very largest or smallest person may not find the seats comfortable but the majority, (90%) of the population, who fall between the 5th and the 95th percentile will be comfortable on them. The handle on a camcorder will fit most hand sizes but not the very largest or smallest. This is designing for the 5th to 95th percentile of the population.

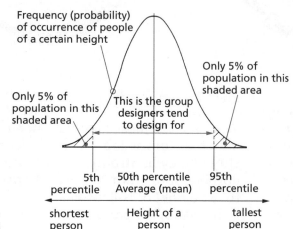

Frequency (probability) of occurrence of people of a certain height

Only 5% of population in this shaded area

Only 5% of population in this shaded area

This is the group designers tend to design for

5th percentile   50th percentile Average (mean)   95th percentile

shortest person   Height of a person   tallest person

Aesthetics

Ben and Katy considered aesthetics right at the beginning of their projects. Here is an **aesthetics checklist** to show you how Ben and Katy developed products which look good.

Aesthetics Checklist

Colour and Shape are the two aesthetic properties which are easiest to understand. Both colour and shape can be used to create **contrast** or **harmony**. Colour is used in both folios at the ideas stages and shapes are the basis for the actual designs.

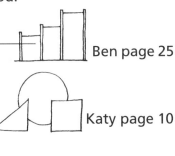

Ben page 25

Katy page 10

Form is three-dimensional and is developed later from the 2-D shapes.

Katy page 12

Proportion Small changes to the proportions of simple shapes can help make designs look elegant, classy, stable or sleek.

This becomes this.

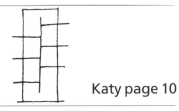

Ben page 25

Balance Most products look balanced or even symmetrical. Experimenting with the balance of shapes and colours can add interest to your design.

Katy page 10

Texture Ben makes excellent use of texture to create a watery theme. Could your design look smooth, textured, hard, soft, glossy or matt? Try using more than one surface texture in your design. It will create contrast and become an eyecatching feature.

Ben page 25

Harmony It may be important to create a design in which all the parts blend in with each other or with the environment in which it will be used. Select harmonious colours or shapes to achieve this.

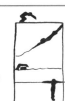

Ben page 25

Contrast Using contrasting colours, textures and shapes can liven up a design and make it more eyecatching. Contrast can help your design to stand out from the rest, e.g. a designer may his design to be **noticed by customers**. Try mixing straight lines and curves in your ideas. The effect can be quite striking.

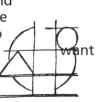

Katy page 10

Pattern Repeating a design feature to create a pattern can help achieve a unified or more organised look. Katy's final design uses a pattern based on squares but only after she has investigated several others in her folio.

Katy page 12

Line Different styles of line can create a formal or an informal look to your design. The effects of using different styles of line can be seen in both folios. Katy uses straight lines inside geometric shapes. Ben represents water with freehand, wavy lines.

Ben page 26

A good way of understanding how aesthetics is used in design is to study how each of these qualities has been used to help design a product (e.g. the inside of a car).

1. IS THE PRODUCT SUITED TO ITS PURPOSE?
(Function and Environment)

If a product is well-designed it will do its job well, e.g. the main **function** of a vacuum cleaner is to remove dirt from a variety of surfaces and floor coverings. Unless it actually does this it is poorly designed. How would you set up a test to compare how well two vacuum cleaners clean? CONSIDER
- Exactly what is the purpose of the product you are evaluating? Remember that products often have both primary and secondary functions, i.e. they do a number of things.
- What tests would you carry out to find out how well the product performs?

2. IS IT EASY TO USE? (Ergonomics)

A well-designed product is easy to use. Ergonomics may well have been an important consideration in its design, e.g. when operating a vacuum cleaner, the user, whatever his or her size, must be able to hold it comfortably, move it around, reach the controls easily and empty it when full. CONSIDER
- Ergonomics.
- Are the controls easy to reach?
- Does it feel comfortable to use?
- Are there any functions that are difficult to operate?

3. IS IT SAFE? (Safety)

All products should be safe to use and be safe when not in use, e.g. accidents frequently happen in homes when small children find, dismantle and swallow things. Designers therefore need to pay close attention to safety considerations when designing products. A can opener may itself be safe but not the sharp edge it leaves on the can. CONSIDER
- Is the product free of dangerous features?
- Is it safe to use?
- Are there warnings given on the product about possible hazards?
- Does it conform to safety standards?

ESSENTIAL INFORMATION

- To find out what is good design, it is useful to have a checklist of seven questions to help you to evaluate a product. Answering the questions will help you to work out whether a product is well designed or badly designed.
- Each question is related to a Design Factor. (See page 33.)

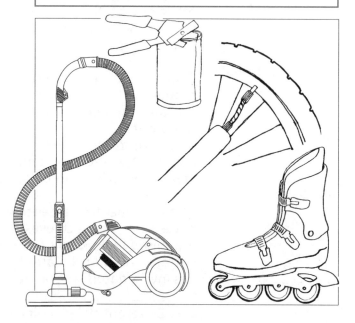

4. IS IT EASY TO MAINTAIN? (Cost)

All products need to be looked after to keep them in good working order, e.g. roller blade wheel bolts need to be checked and tightened and the wheels need to be rotated to avoid uneven wear. CONSIDER
- Are clear instructions provided on how to maintain the product?
- Can you maintain it yourself with ease?
- Do you need specialist tools?
- Is it expensive to replace bits that wear out?

5. DOES IT LOOK GOOD? (Aesthetics)

A well-designed product will look attractive and possibly have a distinctive style. The Dyson vacuum cleaner is a good example of this, which helps to explain why so many Dysons are sold. When evaluating how good a product looks, use the list of headings considered on the 'AESTHETICS' page 35. CONSIDER
- The shape, size, proportions of the product's parts.
- The colours, material and textures.
- Does it have a distinctive style?
- What sort of image does it project?

6. IS IT WELL MADE? (Materials and Construction)

The qualities of the materials and construction used in a product will determine how well it performs and how long it lasts, e.g. a pair of roller blades has a plastic moulded shell, clips and fasteners, a padded lining and wheels that are subject to a lot of hard wear. CONSIDER
- What materials have been used for each part?
- What qualities do these materials have?
- Are the materials suited to their purpose?
- How have the parts been joined together?
- Are there any faults or weaknesses in the product?

7. IS IT GOOD VALUE FOR MONEY? (Cost)

When a consumer buys a product he or she must decide how much to spend. Does he or she spend more on a better quality product that will last longer or save money on what may be an inferior product? For example, when you buy a new pump for your mountain bike, you need to check carefully which pump works best and how well each is made before choosing one from a range of pumps. CONSIDER
- How does the cost of one product compare with others?
- Will it last a long time?
- How well does it do its job?
- Are spare parts costly?

Safety Symbols

These safety symbols are used throughout this Knowledge and Understanding section.

- eye protection
- dust hazard
- ear protection
- electrical hazard
- hold workpiece securely
- beware sharp edges
- beware heat
- protective clothing
- toxic chemicals
- machine tools with moving parts

Types of Wood

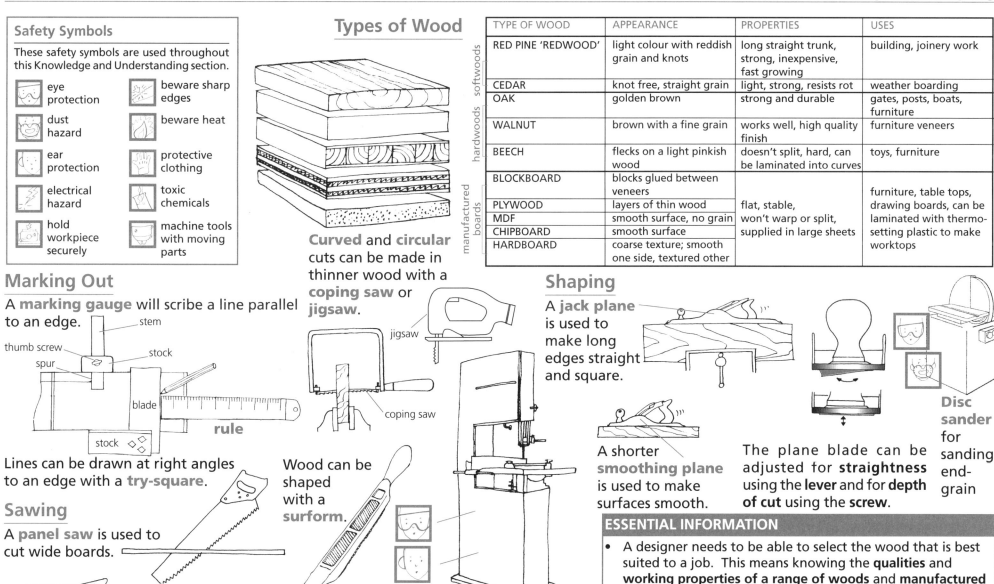

TYPE OF WOOD		APPEARANCE	PROPERTIES	USES
softwoods	RED PINE 'REDWOOD'	light colour with reddish grain and knots	long straight trunk, strong, inexpensive, fast growing	building, joinery work
softwoods	CEDAR	knot free, straight grain	light, strong, resists rot	weather boarding
hardwoods	OAK	golden brown	strong and durable	gates, posts, boats, furniture
hardwoods	WALNUT	brown with a fine grain	works well, high quality finish	furniture veneers
hardwoods	BEECH	flecks on a light pinkish wood	doesn't split, hard, can be laminated into curves	toys, furniture
manufactured boards	BLOCKBOARD	blocks glued between veneers	flat, stable, won't warp or split, supplied in large sheets	furniture, table tops, drawing boards, can be laminated with thermo-setting plastic to make worktops
manufactured boards	PLYWOOD	layers of thin wood	flat, stable, won't warp or split, supplied in large sheets	furniture, table tops, drawing boards, can be laminated with thermo-setting plastic to make worktops
manufactured boards	MDF	smooth surface, no grain	flat, stable, won't warp or split, supplied in large sheets	furniture, table tops, drawing boards, can be laminated with thermo-setting plastic to make worktops
manufactured boards	CHIPBOARD	smooth surface	flat, stable, won't warp or split, supplied in large sheets	furniture, table tops, drawing boards, can be laminated with thermo-setting plastic to make worktops
manufactured boards	HARDBOARD	coarse texture; smooth one side, textured other	flat, stable, won't warp or split, supplied in large sheets	furniture, table tops, drawing boards, can be laminated with thermo-setting plastic to make worktops

Curved and **circular** cuts can be made in thinner wood with a **coping saw** or **jigsaw**.

Marking Out

A **marking gauge** will scribe a line parallel to an edge.

- stem
- thumb screw
- stock
- spur
- blade
- stock
- **rule**

Lines can be drawn at right angles to an edge with a **try-square**.

Sawing

A **panel saw** is used to cut wide boards.

A **tenon saw** is used for accurately cutting out joints and smaller pieces of wood. **Sawing board** or bench hook held in the **wood vice**.

Wood can be shaped with a **surform**.

jigsaw

coping saw

Your teacher will use a **bandsaw** to cut straight and curved shapes in thicker woods.

Shaping

A **jack plane** is used to make long edges straight and square.

A shorter **smoothing plane** is used to make surfaces smooth.

The plane blade can be adjusted for **straightness** using the **lever** and for **depth of cut** using the **screw**.

Disc sander for sanding end-grain

ESSENTIAL INFORMATION

- A designer needs to be able to select the wood that is best suited to a job. This means knowing the **qualities** and **working properties of a range of woods** and **manufactured boards**. The selected piece of timber must be marked out to show the length, width and thickness and any joints required. Various tools and machines are then used to make it straight, smooth and the correct shape.

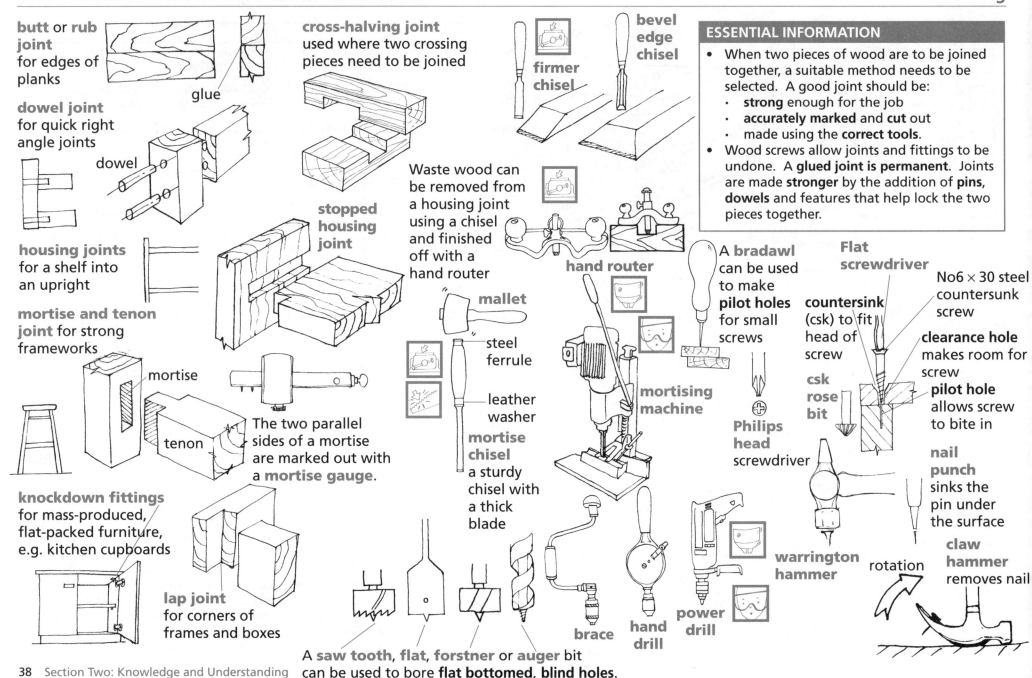

butt or **rub** **joint**
for edges of planks

glue

dowel joint
for quick right angle joints

dowel

housing joints
for a shelf into an upright

mortise and tenon joint for strong frameworks

mortise

tenon

The two parallel sides of a mortise are marked out with a **mortise gauge**.

knockdown fittings
for mass-produced, flat-packed furniture, e.g. kitchen cupboards

lap joint
for corners of frames and boxes

cross-halving joint
used where two crossing pieces need to be joined

stopped housing joint

Waste wood can be removed from a housing joint using a chisel and finished off with a hand router

firmer chisel

bevel edge chisel

mallet
steel ferrule
leather washer

mortise chisel
a sturdy chisel with a thick blade

hand router

mortising machine

A **saw tooth, flat, forstner** or **auger** bit can be used to bore **flat bottomed, blind holes**.

brace

hand drill

power drill

A **bradawl** can be used to make **pilot holes** for small screws

Philips head screwdriver

warrington hammer

Flat screwdriver

countersink (csk) to fit head of screw

csk rose bit

No6 × 30 steel countersunk screw

clearance hole makes room for screw

pilot hole allows screw to bite in

nail punch sinks the pin under the surface

claw hammer removes nail

rotation

ESSENTIAL INFORMATION

- When two pieces of wood are to be joined together, a suitable method needs to be selected. A good joint should be:
  - **strong** enough for the job
  - **accurately marked** and **cut** out
  - made using the **correct tools**.
- Wood screws allow joints and fittings to be undone. A **glued joint is permanent**. Joints are made **stronger** by the addition of **pins**, **dowels** and features that help lock the two pieces together.

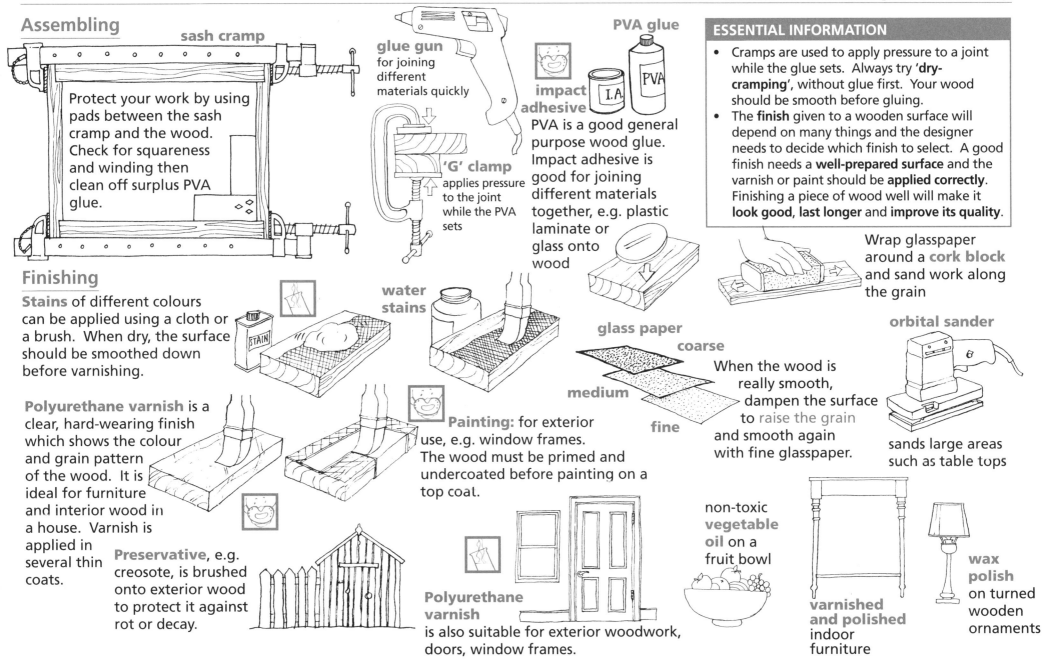

Assembling

sash cramp

Protect your work by using pads between the sash cramp and the wood. Check for squareness and winding then clean off surplus PVA glue.

glue gun
for joining different materials quickly

'G' clamp
applies pressure to the joint while the PVA sets

PVA glue

impact adhesive

PVA is a good general purpose wood glue. Impact adhesive is good for joining different materials together, e.g. plastic laminate or glass onto wood

ESSENTIAL INFORMATION

- Cramps are used to apply pressure to a joint while the glue sets. Always try '**dry-cramping**', without glue first. Your wood should be smooth before gluing.
- The **finish** given to a wooden surface will depend on many things and the designer needs to decide which finish to select. A good finish needs a **well-prepared surface** and the varnish or paint should be **applied correctly**. Finishing a piece of wood well will make it **look good**, **last longer** and **improve its quality**.

Wrap glasspaper around a **cork block** and sand work along the grain

Finishing

Stains of different colours can be applied using a cloth or a brush. When dry, the surface should be smoothed down before varnishing.

Polyurethane varnish is a clear, hard-wearing finish which shows the colour and grain pattern of the wood. It is ideal for furniture and interior wood in a house. Varnish is applied in several thin coats.

Preservative, e.g. creosote, is brushed onto exterior wood to protect it against rot or decay.

water stains

Painting: for exterior use, e.g. window frames. The wood must be primed and undercoated before painting on a top coat.

Polyurethane varnish is also suitable for exterior woodwork, doors, window frames.

glass paper
coarse
medium
fine

When the wood is really smooth, dampen the surface to raise the grain and smooth again with fine glasspaper.

non-toxic **vegetable oil** on a fruit bowl

orbital sander

sands large areas such as table tops

varnished and polished indoor furniture

wax polish on turned wooden ornaments

SAFETY

Always wear a **face mask** or **goggles**.
Tuck in loose clothing (especially ties),
tie back long hair and **wear an apron**.
Before you start turning:
- check the wood is **free from faults**
- check the wood is **securely held**
- **position the tool rest** as near to your wood as possible.
- check that the **turning speed** is correct: slow speed for large work fast speed for small work

PREPARING THE TIMBER

1. Cut more wood than you need to allow for waste at each end.

2. Mark and **saw the diagonals** at each end of the square piece of wood. The cuts will allow the **driving centre** to locate in one end and the revolving centre in the other.

3. Plane the corners of the wood until it is octagonal (i.e. has eight sides).

THE WOOD LATHE

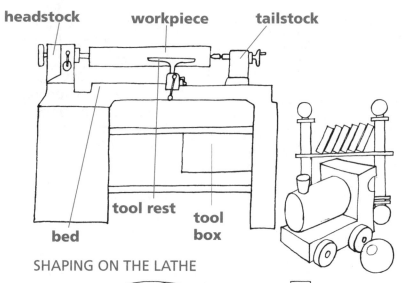

headstock   workpiece   tailstock

tool rest   tool box

bed

SHAPING ON THE LATHE

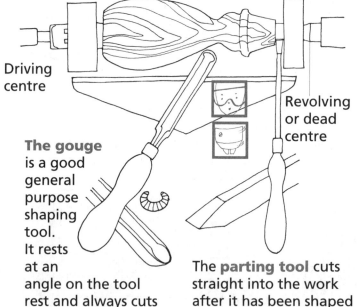

Driving centre

The gouge is a good general purpose shaping tool. It rests at an angle on the tool rest and always cuts with the grain.

Revolving or dead centre

The **parting tool** cuts straight into the work after it has been shaped to remove the waste.

ESSENTIAL INFORMATION

- Round and circular shapes are normally turned out of solid wood on a wood lathe. This process is called wood turning. Wood lathes are used in school workshops by pupils turning a range of items, including parts of wooden toys, wheels and cylinders. Industry uses computer-controlled wood lathes to mass-produce large numbers of turned items such as furniture legs and bannister rails. Wood turning can also be used to create hollow bowls and decorative detail. Blanks of timber are held between centres and spun while various tools remove waste and shape the wood like a chisel. A skilful turner can quickly produce a well-shaped and finished product.

FINISHING ON THE LATHE

Glass paper can be held gently against the spinning work but great care must be taken with this.

Wax polish can be applied to the work using a cloth, **but not while the lathe is spinning**.

Types of Metal

Metals are an important group of materials. They are used to make products as different as aeroplanes, skyscrapers and jewellery. Nearly everything we do, from riding a bike to having a shower, involves the use of metals.

There are four main groups of metals:

Pure Metals
Metals are mined from the earth as ores. Ores are melted in furnaces and refined (cleaned up) to produce pure metals.

Alloys
Metals which have been improved by mixing two or more metals together or by mixing a metal with other elements such as carbon are known as alloys.

Ferrous Metals
These contain iron. Most ferrous metals rust and need to be painted or coated for protection. They are usually magnetic.

Non-Ferrous Metals
These do not contain iron and have better corrosion resistance. Non-magnetic.

Copper, brass and **aluminium** can be **polished** and coated with **clear lacquer** to preserve the shine.

The shapes and forms in which metals can be bought make them easier to use.

ESSENTIAL INFORMATION

- A designer must select the best metal for a job. A job may require a metal which is light or heavy, easily bent, strong, decorative or easily moulded. Some properties can also be improved by the use of heat treatment.

Heat Treatment

Heating and cooling metals in different ways can improve their **properties** and make them easier to use. The main types of heat treatment are **annealing, hardening** and **tempering**.

	Metal	Ferrous	Non-ferrous	Properties	Uses
Pure Metals	Aluminium		✓	Lightweight, easily shaped and formed, low melting point, malleable.	Cooking foil, window frames, drinks cans, castings.
Pure Metals	Copper		✓	Good conductor of heat and electricity, easily bent and shaped, malleable and ductile.	Electric wire, water pipes and boilers.
Alloys	Duralumin (aluminium and copper)		✓	Lightweight and strong. Easily formed and shaped, malleable.	Aircraft parts.
Alloys	Mild Steel (iron and carbon)	✓		Easily welded and formed, needs surface protection, inexpensive.	Car bodies, screws, nuts and bolts.
Alloys	Stainless Steel (steel and chromium)	✓		Good rust resistance, decorative silver colour, shapes and forms well.	Sinks, cutlery, garden forks and spades.
Alloys	Tool Steel (high carbon steel)	✓		Very hard-wearing, can be ground sharp.	Tools such as: files, chisels, saws and screwdrivers
Alloys	Brass (copper and zinc)		✓	Decorative golden colour, casts easily.	Door handles and knockers, screws.

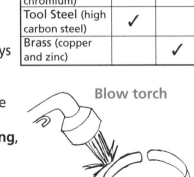

Blow torch

Annealing a beaten copper bangle

ANNEALING: Copper and aluminium **work harden** when beaten and bent. Both metals can be softened (annealed) by heating with a blowtorch and cooling: copper – to a dull red and aluminium – until the soap turns black. This makes these metals **malleable** or **easy to bend** and beat into shape and **ductile, easy to draw into wire.**

HARDENING AND TEMPERING:
Tools made with tool steel are hardened by heating until red hot and cooling quickly in water. Hardening leaves the tools very brittle. The tool must then be tempered by heating slowly until the point reaches the correct colour, then by cooling quickly in water.

Wire
Rod
Tube
Pipe
Angle
Strip
Sheet

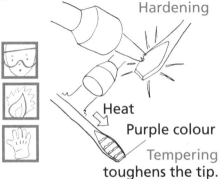

Hardening

Heat

Purple colour

Tempering toughens the tip.

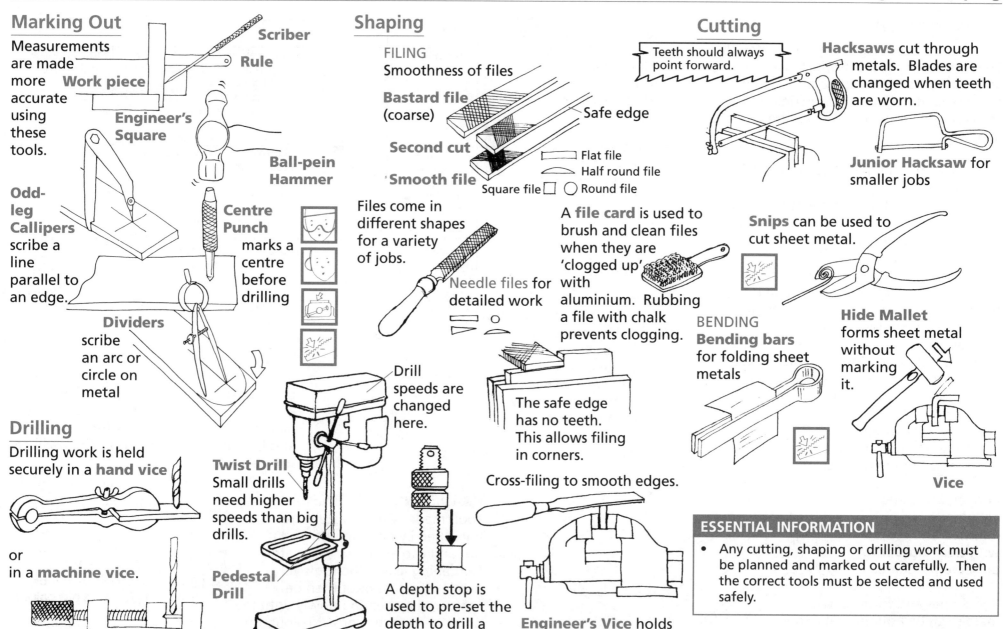

Marking Out

Measurements are made more accurate using these tools.

Scriber

Rule

Work piece

Engineer's Square

Ball-pein Hammer

Odd-leg Callipers scribe a line parallel to an edge.

Centre Punch marks a centre before drilling

Dividers scribe an arc or circle on metal

Drilling

Drilling work is held securely in a **hand vice**

or
in a **machine vice**.

Twist Drill
Small drills need higher speeds than big drills.

Pedestal Drill

Drill speeds are changed here.

Shaping

FILING

Smoothness of files

Bastard file (coarse)

Second cut

Smooth file

Safe edge

▭ Flat file
⌒ Half round file
Square file ☐ ◯ Round file

Files come in different shapes for a variety of jobs.

Needle files for detailed work

A **file card** is used to brush and clean files when they are 'clogged up' with aluminium. Rubbing a file with chalk prevents clogging.

The safe edge has no teeth. This allows filing in corners.

Cross-filing to smooth edges.

A depth stop is used to pre-set the depth to drill a blind hole.

Engineer's Vice holds the work securely.

Cutting

Teeth should always point forward.

Hacksaws cut through metals. Blades are changed when teeth are worn.

Junior Hacksaw for smaller jobs

Snips can be used to cut sheet metal.

BENDING

Bending bars for folding sheet metals

Hide Mallet forms sheet metal without marking it.

Vice

ESSENTIAL INFORMATION

- Any cutting, shaping or drilling work must be planned and marked out carefully. Then the correct tools must be selected and used safely.

Joining

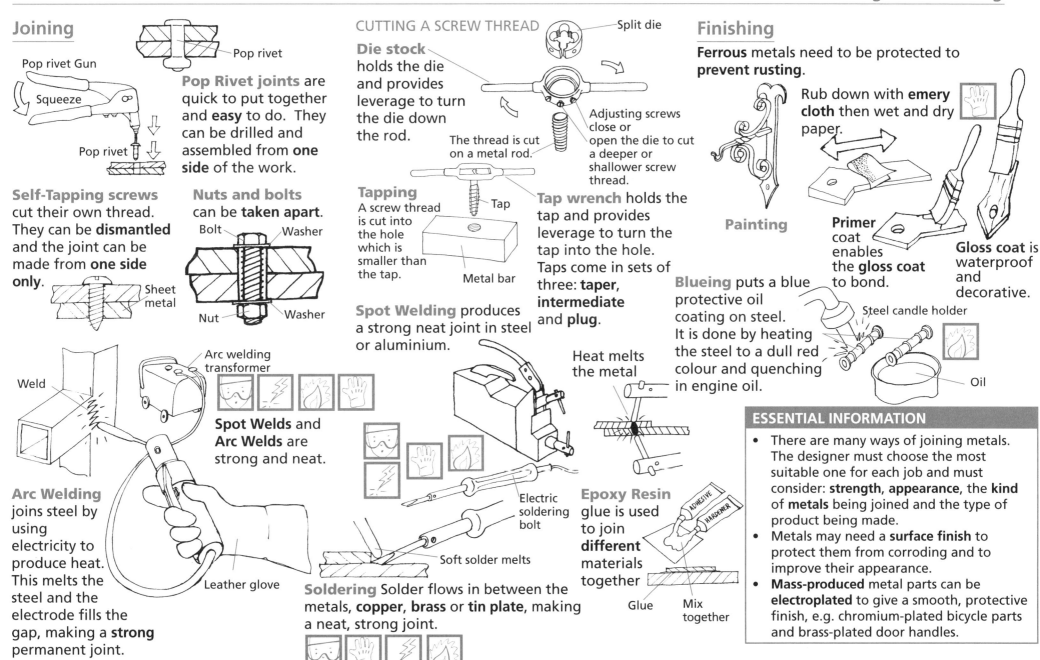

Pop rivet Gun

Squeeze

Pop rivet

Pop rivet

Pop Rivet joints are quick to put together and **easy** to do. They can be drilled and assembled from **one side** of the work.

Self-Tapping screws cut their own thread. They can be **dismantled** and the joint can be made from **one side only**.

Weld

Sheet metal

Nuts and bolts can be **taken apart**.

Bolt
Washer
Nut
Washer

Arc welding transformer

Spot Welds and **Arc Welds** are strong and neat.

Leather glove

Arc Welding joins steel by using electricity to produce heat. This melts the steel and the electrode fills the gap, making a **strong** permanent joint.

CUTTING A SCREW THREAD

Split die

Die stock holds the die and provides leverage to turn the die down the rod.

The thread is cut on a metal rod.

Adjusting screws close or open the die to cut a deeper or shallower screw thread.

Tapping
A screw thread is cut into the hole which is smaller than the tap.

Tap

Metal bar

Tap wrench holds the tap and provides leverage to turn the tap into the hole. Taps come in sets of three: **taper**, **intermediate** and **plug**.

Spot Welding produces a strong neat joint in steel or aluminium.

Heat melts the metal

Electric soldering bolt

Soft solder melts

Soldering Solder flows in between the metals, **copper**, **brass** or **tin plate**, making a neat, strong joint.

Epoxy Resin glue is used to join **different** materials together

ADHESIVE
HARDENER

Glue
Mix together

Finishing

Ferrous metals need to be protected to **prevent rusting**.

Rub down with **emery cloth** then wet and dry paper.

Painting

Primer coat enables the **gloss coat** to bond.

Gloss coat is waterproof and decorative.

Blueing puts a blue protective oil coating on steel. It is done by heating the steel to a dull red colour and quenching in engine oil.

Steel candle holder

Oil

ESSENTIAL INFORMATION

- There are many ways of joining metals. The designer must choose the most suitable one for each job and must consider: **strength**, **appearance**, the **kind of metals** being joined and the type of product being made.
- Metals may need a **surface finish** to protect them from corroding and to improve their appearance.
- **Mass-produced** metal parts can be **electroplated** to give a smooth, protective finish, e.g. chromium-plated bicycle parts and brass-plated door handles.

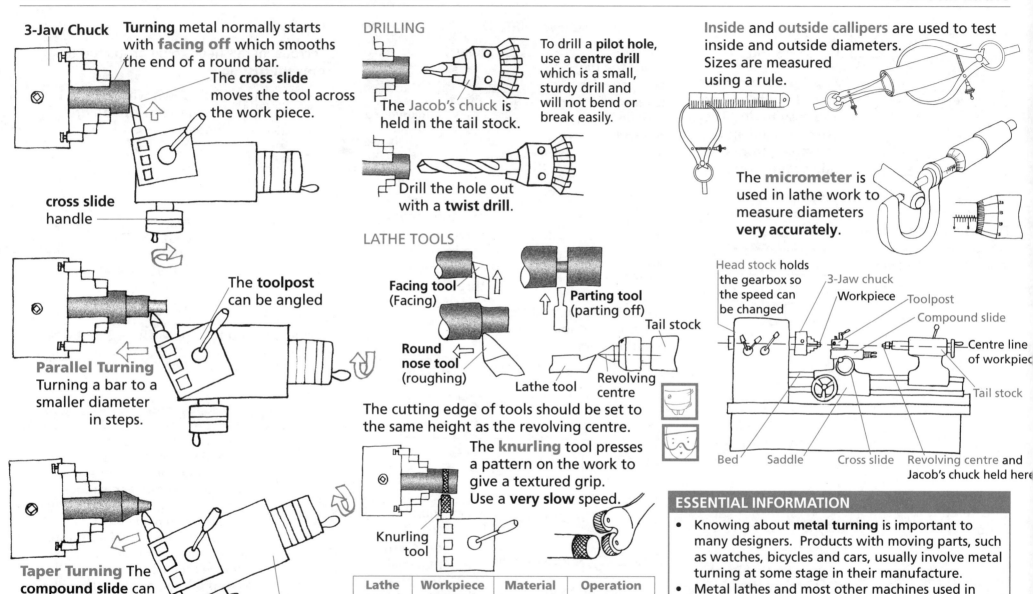

3-Jaw Chuck

Turning metal normally starts with **facing off** which smooths the end of a round bar.

The **cross slide** moves the tool across the work piece.

cross slide handle

Parallel Turning
Turning a bar to a smaller diameter in steps.

The **toolpost** can be angled

Taper Turning The **compound slide** can be angled to cut **tapers** and **chamfers** on a bar.

Compound Slide

DRILLING

To drill a **pilot hole**, use a **centre drill** which is a small, sturdy drill and will not bend or break easily.

The Jacob's chuck is held in the tail stock.

Drill the hole out with a **twist drill**.

LATHE TOOLS

Facing tool (Facing)

Round nose tool (roughing)

Parting tool (parting off)

Tail stock

Lathe tool

Revolving centre

The cutting edge of tools should be set to the same height as the revolving centre.

The **knurling** tool presses a pattern on the work to give a textured grip.
Use a **very slow** speed.

Knurling tool

Lathe speed	Workpiece diameter	Material	Operation
slow ↓ fast	large ↓ small	mild steel brass aluminium	knurling roughing cut finishing cut

Inside and **outside callipers** are used to test inside and outside diameters. Sizes are measured using a rule.

The **micrometer** is used in lathe work to measure diameters **very accurately**.

Head stock holds the gearbox so the speed can be changed

3-Jaw chuck

Workpiece

Toolpost

Compound slide

Centre line of workpiece

Tail stock

Bed   Saddle   Cross slide   Revolving centre and Jacob's chuck held here

ESSENTIAL INFORMATION

- Knowing about **metal turning** is important to many designers. Products with moving parts, such as watches, bicycles and cars, usually involve metal turning at some stage in their manufacture.
- Metal lathes and most other machines used in modern industry can be controlled by computers. These are called **C.N.C.** or Computer Numerically Controlled machines. This makes **mass production** cheaper and improves the quality of the product.

Casting

Metal shapes are produced by pouring molten metal into **moulds** made of damp casting sand.

1. A smooth wooden **pattern** the same as the final casting is placed on a flat board.

2. An open-ended metal box called a **drag** is placed over it and packed with **damp casting sand**.

3. The whole thing is turned upside down and another box, known as a **cope**, is placed on top. **Parting sand** is sprinkled over the surface, then this, too, is packed with sand around two **sprue pins**.

4. The **cope** and **drag** are separated and the **pattern** and **sprue pins** removed. The **parting sand** eases separation.

5. The **cope** and **drag** are put back together and **molten brass** or **aluminium** is poured in and allowed to cool. In schools, **aluminium** is used. It has a **low melting point**.

The aluminium or brass is melted, **de-gassed** then poured from the **crucible** into the **runner** until the metal fills the **riser**.

upside down drag

cope

sprue pins

air vent

drag

crucible

runner

riser

ESSENTIAL INFORMATION
• Complex, solid metal shapes which are difficult to make by any other means need to be **cast**.
• **Forging** is done to make steel bars and strips **stronger** and more **decorative**.

A good pattern has got sloping sides and rounded internal corners.

Cross-section of mould ready for pouring the metal

Air vents to allow gas to escape

riser

runner

cope

drag

6. **Runner** and **riser** are cut off.

Products like this door knocker are made by casting.

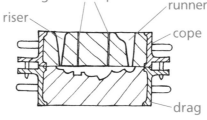

Mass-produced items (e.g. alloy pencil sharpeners) are often die-cast in reusable moulds.

Forging

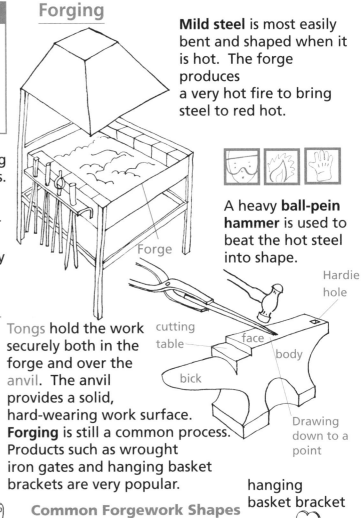

Forge

Mild steel is most easily bent and shaped when it is hot. The forge produces a very hot fire to bring steel to red hot.

A heavy **ball-pein hammer** is used to beat the hot steel into shape.

Hardie hole

Tongs hold the work securely both in the forge and over the anvil. The anvil provides a solid, hard-wearing work surface. **Forging** is still a common process. Products such as wrought iron gates and hanging basket brackets are very popular.

cutting table

face

body

bick

Drawing down to a point

Common Forgework Shapes

hanging basket bracket

point   **eye**   **scroll**   **twist**

Oil is the main source of **plastics**. Companies like ICI change oil into plastic granules. The granules are produced in many colours and are sold to manufacturers who use heat and **injection-moulding** machines to shape them into everyday products.

Types of Plastic

There are two main types of plastic:

Thermosetting plastics are **heat resistant**, **hard-wearing**, easily cleaned and can be **coloured**. They are ideal for pot handles, light switches and **plastic laminate** kitchen worktops, e.g. Melamine and Urea Formaldehyde.

A product made from thermosetting plastic will not soften with heat.

Thermoplastics

Most of the plastics you work with in school are thermoplastics. They go soft when heated and can be bent or formed into shapes. You will probably make a model with clear or coloured **acrylic** sheet. This is a **thermoplastic**. Everyday products made from thermoplastics include **polypropylene** chairs, toothbrushes and telephones. Other thermoplastics include polystyrene, ABS, Polyvinyl Chloride (PVC).

Marking Out

Acrylic sheet comes with a protective coating. Try to leave this on for as long as possible.

Protective polythene coating

Mark out bends, holes and cuts with a spirit-based fineline pen on the protective coat.

Cutting

Straight cuts can be scored with a **plastic cutter** and snapped in a vice or over the edge of a bench. Line up with the edge of the bench. Hold firmly and snap.

Curves are cut using a fine-toothed **coping saw** or **abrafile**. Small, straight cuts can be made with a hacksaw.

Finishing the edges

Smoothing is done by
1. **cross filing**, then
2. **draw filing**, then
3. using **wet** and **dry** abrasive paper, and finally
4. polishing the edge with **finishing paste**.

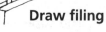

Draw filing

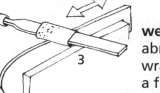

wet and dry abrasive paper wrapped around a file

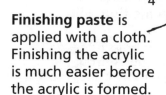

Finishing paste is applied with a cloth. Finishing the acrylic is much easier before the acrylic is formed.

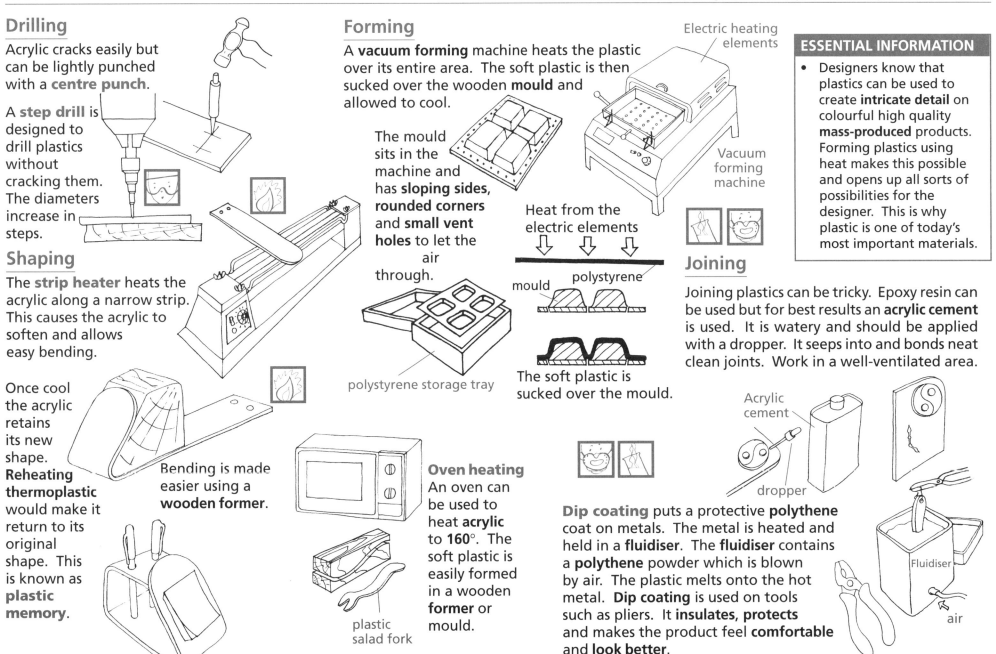

Drilling

Acrylic cracks easily but can be lightly punched with a **centre punch**.

A **step drill** is designed to drill plastics without cracking them. The diameters increase in steps.

Shaping

The **strip heater** heats the acrylic along a narrow strip. This causes the acrylic to soften and allows easy bending.

Once cool the acrylic retains its new shape. **Reheating thermoplastic** would make it return to its original shape. This is known as **plastic memory**.

Bending is made easier using a **wooden former**.

Forming

A **vacuum forming** machine heats the plastic over its entire area. The soft plastic is then sucked over the wooden **mould** and allowed to cool.

The mould sits in the machine and has **sloping sides, rounded corners** and **small vent holes** to let the air through.

polystyrene storage tray

Electric heating elements

Vacuum forming machine

Heat from the electric elements

mould   polystyrene

The soft plastic is sucked over the mould.

Oven heating
An oven can be used to heat **acrylic** to **160°**. The soft plastic is easily formed in a wooden **former** or mould.

plastic salad fork

ESSENTIAL INFORMATION

- Designers know that plastics can be used to create **intricate detail** on colourful high quality **mass-produced** products. Forming plastics using heat makes this possible and opens up all sorts of possibilities for the designer. This is why plastic is one of today's most important materials.

Joining

Joining plastics can be tricky. Epoxy resin can be used but for best results an **acrylic cement** is used. It is watery and should be applied with a dropper. It seeps into and bonds neat clean joints. Work in a well-ventilated area.

Acrylic cement

dropper

Dip coating puts a protective **polythene** coat on metals. The metal is heated and held in a **fluidiser**. The **fluidiser** contains a **polythene** powder which is blown by air. The plastic melts onto the hot metal. **Dip coating** is used on tools such as pliers. It **insulates, protects** and makes the product feel **comfortable** and **look better**.

Fluidiser

air

Exam Papers

There are three exam papers, one at each of the three levels: Foundation, General and Credit. You will sit either Foundation and General, or General and Credit. Your teacher will discuss them with you after your prelim exams. It is important that you take your teacher's advice about which two papers you will sit and that you discuss your choice with your parents. The duration of each paper is 1 hour and the marks are roughly the same, around 60 marks for each paper.

Exam Topics

The questions covered by the exams will always be from the following nine topics:

1. Common materials, their properties and uses
2. Manufacturing processes
3. Surface finishing
4. Common hand tools
5. Common machine tools and equipment
6. Designing
7. Factors which influence design
8. Stages of planning for manufacture
9. Safety in the workshop.

Study one topic at a time and plan your study in your Study Planner.

STUDY PLANNER						
DAY/DATE	9.30-10.30	11.00-12.00	1.30-2.30	3.00-4.00	6.00-7.00	7.30-8.00
Sat. 13th	CHEM (molecules)	MATHS (geometry)	C&D (handtools)	GEOG (crops)	visit gran	art
mon. 15th	school	remember maths H/work			C&D (design)	phys. (elect)
tues. 16th						

Study Tips

- Start your revision as early as possible in the course. This will help prepare you well and build your confidence.
- Choose a study room which is quiet and comfortable.
- Make sure all the materials you need, including pens, pencils and paper, are available at your study table.
- Work out your best times of the day for studying.
- Try to study for about one hour at a time with breaks in between.
- Plan your study time on a study planner. This saves time and mental energy during the study sessions.
- Practise on previous exam papers and make good use of the prelim and mock exams at school.

ESSENTIAL INFORMATION

- The exam papers test your Knowledge and Understanding of Craft & Design.
- The grade you will be awarded after your exam papers are marked is one third of your final grade. This grade is counted along with your Design Folio grade and your Practical Project grade. An average is taken and this becomes your overall grade.
- It is important then that you plan your study time and prepare well for your exams.

Exam Technique

- Ensure you know the date, time and place of your exams as far in advance as possible.
- Avoid being late – rushing around will only make you nervous.
- Do only light revision the night before the exam and on exam day. This will keep your mind fresh.
- Organise your exam equipment, e.g. pens, pencils, rubber, sharpener, calculator, early!
- Read the instructions on your exam paper carefully. Re-reading them is time well spent.
- Answer easier questions first. Don't get bogged down with difficult questions. Come back to them later.
- Keep your answers neat and tidy.
- Spend a little more time thinking about the question. This can save time when writing the answer.
- Take all the time given for the exam. But try to leave time at the end to check your answers.
- Examiners look for quality, not quantity. Make sure you answer what has been asked. Don't just write all you know about each topic.